D1131763

Thomas Adams, Ph.D.
**Professor and Associate Chairperson
for Undergraduate Education
Department of Physiology
Michigan State University
East Lansing, MI 48824-1101**

TEMPERATURE
AND HUMAN LIFE

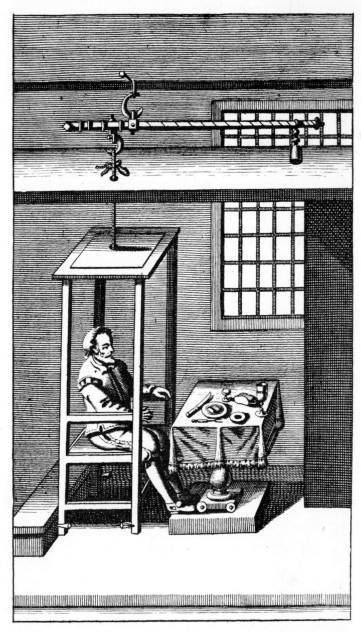

Sanctorius and his balance for the measurement of insensible perspiration. The first quantitative study of physiological hygiene (1614). Reproduced from *Medicina Statica*, translated into English by John Quincy. Fourth edition, London, 1728.

TEMPERATURE
AND
HUMAN LIFE

BY

C.-E. A. WINSLOW

AND

L. P. HERRINGTON

1949

PRINCETON UNIVERSITY PRESS

PRINCETON, NEW JERSEY

PRINTED IN THE UNITED STATES OF AMERICA
BY THE COLONIAL PRESS INC., CLINTON, MASS.

PREFACE

MODERN physiology may be dated from 1628, when William Harvey published his monograph on the circulation of the blood; but in 1614 Sanctorius, in his *Medicina Statica* (from which the frontispiece of the present volume is reproduced) had already laid the basis for experimental hygiene. Since the days of Harvey, progress in the science of physiology has been promptly mirrored in applications to the art of medicine. In the field of physiological hygiene, however, the case has been very different.

One vital factor in the maintenance of health, nutrition, has made spectacular advances during recent years as a result of close and intimate contact between theory and practice. In other fields, such as air conditioning, exercise and rest, sleeping and waking, the teachings given under the name of "physiological hygiene" are generally of an empirical nature and in some cases have not progressed much beyond the *obiter dicta* of Galen.

The early development of the profession of the Heating and Ventilating Engineer took place under the quite erroneous concept that the object of ventilation was to dilute organic poisons formed in the breath. Fortunately it happened that the procedures used to ventilate removed excessive heat given off from the body, as well as chemical substances from the mouth and nose. Furthermore, the American Society of Heating and Ventilating Engineers had the remarkable foresight thirty years ago to establish a research laboratory in which highly significant elementary physiological studies were begun.

When the John B. Pierce Laboratory of Hygiene was established in 1933, it seemed that the time had come for a planned attack on the problem involved in man's relation to his thermal environment, in which both physiological reactions and physical stimuli should be given due and adequate weight. With an associate, A. P. Gagge (now Lieutenant-Colonel in the United States Army), and the present authors, the staff included the threefold approach of physics, physiology, and environmental hygiene; and the results, we believe, achieved a desirable clarification of the subject in hand and laid the basis for a sound solution of the problems in the field of air conditioning.

Chapter I of the present book deals with background knowledge in the field of metabolism, the physiological process which is the basis of life, and also with the reasons why air conditioning is so important. Chapters II and III summarize the information accumulated by us and by others (particularly E. F. DuBois) on the basic problems of thermal interchange between the body and its environment, the mechanism by which the body adjusts itself to that environment, and the limits of such adjustment. In this field, it has been possible to develop experimental techniques (which we have called "partitional calorimetry") capable of adaptation to many other problems besides those already solved and to derive simple mathematical formulas by which the influence of various atmospheric conditions upon individuals operating at various metabolic rates can be predicted with a high degree of accuracy.

The intense interest aroused during the war in the adjustment of military personnel to extremes of heat or cold stimulated an enormous amount of fruitful research on the physiology of clothing; and in this field too, the Laboratory of Hygiene had the privilege of playing a part. Some of the major conclusions reached on this subject are summarized in Chapter IV.

In Chapter V we have outlined the fundamental objectives to be attained in the air conditioning of occupied spaces; and in Chapter VI we have reviewed very briefly the procedures by which the heating and ventilating engineer is prepared to meet those needs.

Finally, in Chapter VII, we have presented a survey of the vast amount of uncorrelated information available with regard to the air conditioning of the outside world in which we live. Climate and season remain among the most important factors in human health and welfare. The prevalence of infections of the upper respiratory tract in winter is still the outstanding problem of epidemiology. One of us has worked on this problem for over forty years. It has been illuminated by the fruitful contributions of the late Ellsworth Huntington, and it has been confused and misrepresented by other and less scientific writers. We believe that the data which we have summarized from many sources deserve the attention of the epidemiologist.

A considerable portion of the material covered in Chapters I to VII has an important educational application in the fields of environmental physiology and physiological hygiene as these topics are treated in relation to the general field of public health. Both authors have made wide use of this material in graduate seminars conducted in the Department of Public Health at Yale University, and have found that it provides a much needed quantitative background for the many problems in physiological hygiene which are related to climate and thermal stress.

The References are listed alphabetically at the end of the book, and the superscript numbers in the text refer to this list. It was thought that it would be more convenient to workers in this field to have the bibliography all together, rather than scattered through the book in footnotes.

For the opportunity to carry out our own studies, and to prepare the present volume, we are deeply indebted to Mr. Clarence M. Woolley and his colleagues, Mr. Rolland J. Hamilton and Mr. Henry L. Weimer, Trustees of the John B. Pierce Foundation, and in later years to Mr. J. F. O'Brien, Director of that Foundation. The purpose for which John B.

Pierce created his endowment was "the promotion of research, educational, technical, or scientific work in the general field of heating, ventilation, and sanitation for the increase of knowledge to the end that the general hygiene and comfort of human beings and their habitations may be advanced." It was a sound and penetrating vision which saw that advance in this important field of practical achievement depended on a basic understanding of the physiological factors. For this opportunity we express our deep appreciation.

The work along these lines has been only begun. We heartily concur with Prof. Lawrence Irving of Swarthmore, who has recently said: "There is need for educational institutions in physiology more elementary, more nearly basic, and much broader in scope than those now provided by medicine. I suggest that institutions and departments are particularly needed for descriptive physiology and for studies preparing physiologists to investigate the life of all animals in the field in all environments and conditions. The facilities for broadening physiological training are largely waiting unused by physiologists in institutions for natural history and in the military establishments. Their employment for physiological explorations upon a scale of world-wide interest and usefulness requires ventures outside of the laboratory, and promises intellectual adventures upon exciting frontiers of physiology."

C.-E. A. WINSLOW
L. P. HERRINGTON

John B. Pierce Laboratory of Hygiene
New Haven, Connecticut

CONTENTS

CONTENTS

The Man-made Climate of Interior Spaces

*TEMPERATURE
AND HUMAN LIFE*

CHAPTER I

PRODUCTION OF HEAT IN THE LIFE PROCESS

Man as a Machine

ANIMALS, including human beings, as well as plants are all extremely complex; and to call them "living machines" suggests mental images which are quite unduly simplified. Yet in a basic sense living things are subject to certain of the limitations of simpler machines. They certainly obey the fundamental laws of physics, and a comprehension of those laws is essential in modern physiology.

Perhaps no term in common use has had a more fascinating history than the word "energy," with its related terms, power and work. In common parlance we need to gain energy in order to do work. The Greek philosopher-scientists, who applied the term "power" to the property in food which gave the body life, motion, and heat, were influenced in their conclusions by practical observations which are familiar to everyone. Perhaps they observed an uncleared field and a dozen slave laborers set to work upon it. In due time, the field was cleared and planted at a cost of 25 bushels of wheat consumed by the laborers. Mystical views of vital forces may prevail in moments of relaxation, but the practical man has recognized for centuries the rather exact physiological accounting that relates food to bodily heat and motion, and to practical work done on the environment. The equating of 100 stumps removed to 25 bushels of wheat, or 100 leagues marched by 10,000 men to 300 tons of wheat consumed by them, are examples of physiological arithmetic quite analogous to those which are solved more accurately by the modern physiologist or nutritionist.

The Concept of Energy

In spite of these fundamental approaches to the problem, practiced with approximate correctness for centuries, the definition of the intrinsic property involved—energy, power, heat, or motion—was only slowly reduced to a convenient concept. Until a century ago, energy was regarded as an intangible property transferred to material bodies when work is done upon them, and passed on to other bodies of matter on which the energized body itself, in turn, does work. If a free body of material was put in motion by a steady force of 10 pounds and moved 100 feet, the work accomplished was regarded as 10 × 100 feet, or 1000 foot-pounds. If, by collision, this moving body transferred its energy to another, the energy of 1000 foot-pounds was regarded as something transferred and conserved in the process. This very serviceable elementary definition relating energy to work is still exemplified in the use of work units such as the foot-pound, kilogram-calorie, etc. However, the discovery of the equivalence of heat and energy by Joule in the nineteenth century, and recognition of the fact that there is a form of energy, namely light, which passes through space apparently without association with matter, gradually required the acceptance of the view that energy had an objective existence of its own, coordinate with that of matter itself. Many scientific observations of the association of matter and energy finally led, in the nineteenth century, to a doctrine of the conservation of energy.

It is difficult for the modern mind to realize the reluctance with which such concepts were accepted. In the last hundred years the acceleration of commercial exchanges and business practice in the western world and the advance of popular acquaintance with the objective elements of science have ingrained even in the lay mind a passive acceptance of the notion that every process involves a quid pro quo. In such a public atmosphere the notion that there is a universal principle imposing an exact accounting on movements of matter and energy and managing at all times an exact balance of cosmic assets seems both natural and unremarkable. Nonetheless, the proposals by Mayer, Joule, and Helmholtz in the nineteenth century relative to the conservation of energy in the universe were greeted with coolness and skepticism. Joule, on presenting his paper on this subject before the British Academy of Science, was interrupted and asked to be brief, and Helmholtz's original presentation of his theory was published in pamphlet form at his own expense.[31]

Yet scientific thought moves always onward. Almost before the biological community has had time to reap the full fruit of this principle of matter-energy conservation, we find that new developments in physical theory require a considerable revision of that principle itself.

As we are all aware, modern physics since Einstein has repudiated the *separate* "laws" of the conservation of energy and the conservation of matter. Energy is now said to possess inertia and gravitational attraction so that 1 gram of matter has the same inertia and gravitational attraction as c^2 ergs, or 8.986 $\times$ 10^{13} joules of energy. Furthermore, energy and matter no longer are confined to their separate and perpetually unaltered totals, as required by the nineteenth century doctrines of the conservation of energy and the conservation of matter. Rather, we have accomplished the conversion of matter into energy (the atomic bomb), and vice versa, although to this date the atomic physicists have not materialized an orange, a rabbit, a pound of iron, or any other item of matter as impressive as the tremendous energy they have released by the destruction of matter. All this is entirely in keeping with the philosophy of the Red Queen, who screamed vigorously sometime before her finger was pricked and reproved Alice's astonishment at this order of events, observing that it's a very poor rule that doesn't work both ways.

It is difficult to say just what effect these latest chapters in the history of energy and matter will have on the physiological treatment of man's energy processes. Perhaps the processes which provide man with heat and motion as a result of his internal chemical and physical reactions with food require much further analysis on the plane of the classical notions of the matter-energy association before they can be treated in terms of the newer physical concepts. Perhaps the level of organization in these biological energy processes is such that the classical notions will retain status as economical and serviceable descriptions. Perhaps not.

Energy Needs of the Body

In any case, it is clear that the simple dynamic relationship between energy and work is basic in the understanding of human metabolism on an immediate practical plane. Recognition of the fact that full combustion of a foodstuff in a bomb calorimeter and in the human body produced the same amount of heat was a major advance. Only when this cornerstone was securely embedded in physiological thinking was it possible to make substantial scientific progress.

Nutrition has, of course, a qualitative as well as a quantitative aspect. The body requires salts, vitamins, amino acids, and fatty acids essential to the rebuilding of body tissues, as well as calories of energy; but with this problem we are not concerned in the present discussion.

In spite of all advances in physical theory, it is clear that for practical purposes the comparison of man's energy processes to those of the heat engine is justified by the fact that in both the heat engine and in man it is possible to relate the initial and final energy content of the fuel to work done and heat dissipated. There are, however, notable differences in detail. In the human organism the relatively simple temperature degradation process of the heat engine is replaced by a tremendously complex series of physicochemical reactions occur-

ring at essentially a constant temperature and collectively referred to as the intermediary metabolism. In this process the
human body is considerably more efficient than the simple
steam engine. Ordinarily about twenty per cent of the energy
value of food can be converted into useful work as against a
value of about fourteen per cent for the efficiency of the steam
engine. It has also been determined that if the temperature of
food combustion in the cells of the body followed the rule
applicable to heat engines, we would expect this cell temperature to be of the order of 238°F (114.5°C). Hence, in a
number of substantial ways the production of heat and energy
during metabolic processes is qualitatively different from the
simple combustion processes of familiar machines.

The diversity of these metabolic processes, the low temperature at which they proceed, and their selectivity with respect
to fuel (the qualitative aspect of nutrition) appear to be the
chief characteristics which distinguish "vital" from "non-vital"
combustion processes. None of the observations in this field
are more intriguing than those dealing with preference of
biological systems for certain types of molecular arrangement
in their foodstuffs. Compounds of the same general molecular
arrangement may occur which are mirror images of one another in spatial configuration. When such general compounds
are synthesized in the laboratory, these spatially contrasting
forms occur in equal proportions. In plant and animal cells,
however, such syntheses proceed asymmetrically with a preference for one of the possible orientations; and when animals are
fed compounds containing both forms of a general molecular
plan, they are often able to select from the molecular mixture
the asymmetric form typically produced by living matter and
to reject the form that is not of natural biological occurrence.
If we were firing the boiler of a steam engine with scrap from
a furniture factory and noted that wood screws threaded from
left to right burned while those threaded from right to left
came out unscathed, we would most certainly be astonished.

Yet in its appetite for arrangement as well as potential fuel value and general molecular constitution, living matter exhibits a similar selectivity.

In spite of all such differences in detail, the broad relationship between food, heat, and work remains unshaken. The movements of living things, the contraction of muscles, and the beating of the heart require energy, and so do the processes of growth and repair, the constant building and rebuilding of the manifold tissues of which the body is composed. The source of this energy is food; and the process by which the energy is liberated is a combination of food elements with the oxygen taken in with the breath, just as the energy liberated by burning fuel is liberated by union with oxygen. The whole life process is a form of slow combustion; and it ultimately leads, in the body as in the heat machine, to the production of work and heat. There are definite quantitative relationships between the intake of food and oxygen on the one hand and work done and heat liberated on the other. This process is called "metabolism," and it is the basic process in physiology, on which all other physiological processes depend.

Early Concepts of Metabolism

The Greek authors of ancient times had fascinating glimpses of some parts of the truth about this fundamental process.[129] Throughout the Hippocratic essay on "Nutriment," the word "power" is used in relation to nutrition. The author tells us that "Power gives to all things increase, nourishment and birth," that "Nourishment is sometimes into growth and being, sometimes into being only, as is the case with old men; sometimes in addition it is into strength." Even a quantitative relation between food and energy is suggested in the phrase, "It is a great thing successfully to adapt quantity to power." Galen, in the first century A.D., tells us, "Whatever in the blood is fatty, light and tenuous, becomes in the warmer bodies, a kind of fuel for the heat"; and "all nutriment, as implied by the very word, increases the heat of the animal . . .

8

and likewise it truly heats the body which it nourishes." Again, he says, "Since daily a large part of their substance flows away from all living things on account of innate heat, concoction is very necessary to their body, wherefore there is need of food and drink, that the just measure of heat may be preserved." He even notes that "The quantity of food must correspond in proportion to the quantity of perspiration."

For the other factor in metabolism, that related to respiration, ancient interpretations were much less clear. The classical writers thought of respiration as a source of nutritive elements, a medium for the removal of waste produce, and a device for cooling the body. The Hippocratic essay on "Breaths" tells us that "bodies of men and of animals, generally, are nourished by three kinds of nourishment, and the names thereof are solid food, drink, and wind." In "Nutriment" it is stated that "The lungs draw a nourishment which is the opposite of that of the body." Galen points out that respiration rates, like food requirements, vary with age and activity: "you may observe that with those who exercise and bathe, and those who in any other manner are heated, not only does the respiration become faster and denser, but the pulse is changed likewise." Furthermore, while he nowhere visualizes such a process as oxidation, he does make strikingly suggestive comparisons with combustion outside the body. In one place he says, "For bitumen, resin, tallow, oil, and pitch are hot in power, because they easily become hot in actuality and in fact they very quickly take fire: besides when they are applied to our bodies, they plainly give heat." Again, "I think they are most inclined to these ideas by the things that are evident about flames; for we plainly see the latter perish as quickly when deprived of air as living things; as medicinal cupping glasses show and all narrow and hollow objects which, when put over flames, prevent their breathing and easily extinguish them. If, therefore, it be discovered what flames in such situations undergo when they are extinguished, perhaps it will be possible to find also what use the heat in living things makes of respiration." This is a really admirable piece of scientific reasoning. It shows how far physiological thinking had progressed, and how it was held up by the backwardness of chemistry.

Another suggestive passage: "Where that which requires the use is greatest, there also it is not unreasonable for the use itself to be much increased, for a greater flame needs more abundant air, a smaller, less." Again, respiration is cut off and the innate heat is extinguished from excess of cold matter "just as a flame is put out by much damp wood."

The major defect of Greek science, in this as in other fields, was the almost complete lack of quantitative data. A single almost unique example of quantitative physiology is that claimed for Erisistratus in the third century, B.C. He is said by Heidel [52] to have experimented with a respiration calorimeter, placing hens and other fowls in a jar, first feeding and weighing them; then, after an interval of time, removing them and weighing them again with their visible excreta. The net loss of weight represented what was later called "insensible perspiration."

Development of Modern Knowledge of Metabolism

For definite and proven advance in this field, we must jump over nearly two thousand years. The *Ars de Statica Medicina* of Sanctorius, published in 1614 at Padua, represents the first major contribution to experimental hygiene in medical history, a contribution ranking close to Harvey's pioneer work in experimental physiology. Sanctorius devised the first clinical thermometer, but his most important work was the repetition and expansion with the human subject of the observations attributed to Erisistratus. He constructed a large steel yard supporting a platform on which he sat for hours and observed the gain in weight when he took food and the loss of weight (called "insensible perspiration") during periods when no food was taken and no sensible evacuation from the body occurred. He estimated this loss by insensible perspiration at 5 pounds a day, and distinguished between the loss from the external skin and that from the upper respiratory tract (which latter he estimated at half a pound). He emphasized the importance of maintaining a reasonably constant weight, and advised eating such food and observing such a regimen as would establish a desirable mean loss of weight by insensible perspiration. All in all, Sanctorius had a logical and clear conception of metabolism on the basis of conservation of matter and of the essential correspondence between food intake, bodily activity, and evaporative loss. His whole physiological theory was based on the use of the balance, and even when he speaks of the spirits being made "light" or "heavy," he is not using merely metaphorical terms. To have established biological experimentation on so frank a quantitative basis was no mean achievement in the seventeenth century.

To supplement the idea of the conservation of matter by conservation of energy, in human physiology, required advances in chemistry not yet available.

John Mayow, in 1668, outlined the correct approach to this problem by concluding that a candle ultimately went out in a confined space "because it is deprived of its aerial sustenance or food." This food he described as composed of "igneo-aereal particles" (an excellent scientific description), and he explained respiration as "the separation of the air by the lungs and the intermixture with the blood mass of certain particles absolutely necessary to animal life." This was in a sense the discovery of oxygen and of its role in combustion and respiration.

Unfortunately, in 1697 Stahl advanced a different theory which greatly confused scientific thinking on this point for nearly a century. He maintained that when a substance burned it gave off a hypothetical gas which he named "phlogiston"; and normal air, able to support combustion, was called "dephlogisticated air." This theory, too, could be interpreted in modern scientific terms by identifying "phlogiston" with carbon dioxide, which is produced by combustion and respiration. Yet emphasis on the idea that the air of a confined space in which combustion had taken place was no longer able to support combustion because of the positive presence of "phlogiston" rather than to the absence of "igneo-aereal" particles led some of the most brilliant pioneers in chemical science far astray. Lusk points out[74] that Black, in 1757, actually discovered carbon dioxide and that Priestly, in 1774, rediscovered oxygen. In 1777 Scheele performed an ingenious experiment with bees in which we can now see that the exhaustion of oxygen by respiration and its replacement by carbon dioxide was demonstrated. Adair Crawford, in 1779, actually performed calorimetric experiments with animals in which he demonstrated that "the quantity of heat produced when a given quantity of pure air is altered by the respiration of an animal is nearly equal to that which is produced when the same quantity of air is altered by the combustion of wax or charcoal"; and that "when an animal is placed in a cold medium, it phlogisticates a greater quantity of air in a given time than when it is placed in a warm medium." During this period of twenty years all the data were available for a rational exploration of metabolism, but the inverted "phlogiston" theory (which all these workers accepted) prevented any such explanation. This is one of the most interesting examples in the history of science of the confusion created by an unsound theoretical conception.

It remained for two great Frenchmen, A. L. Lavoisier and P. S. Laplace in France to work out the real nature of combustion and respiration. It was Lavoisier, in 1775, who finally and definitely discovered oxygen, although Mayow, Priestly, and Scheele had worked with it without recognizing its nature, and thus the phlogiston theory was finally overthrown. The monograph by Lavoisier and Laplace, "Memoire sur la Chaleur," [70] is rightly described by Jacques Loeb as the foundation of scientific biology. Using an ice calorimeter, the great chemist and the great astronomer demonstrated for the first time that combustion and respiration were essentially similar processes, both based on a chemical reaction between an active constituent making up about a quarter of the atmosphere (oxygen in our terminology) and some constituent of the burning substance or the respiring body. The authors conclude that "Respiration is then a combustion, of a very slow type, it is true, but otherwise entirely comparable with the burning of carbon; it takes place in the interior of the lungs, without producing observable light because the substance of the heat, when freed, is immediately absorbed by the humidity of the organism concerned; the heat developed in this combustion is communicated to the blood passing through the lungs and thence is distributed throughout the whole animal body. Thus, the air which we breathe serves two objectives, equally essential for our survival; it removes from the blood the basis of fixed air which in excess would be very harmful; and the heat which this chemical combustion liberates in the lungs, makes good the continual loss of heat which we suffer to the atmosphere and to the surrounding bodies." Lavoisier even demonstrated the increases in oxygen consumption due to ingestion of food and to decrease in atmospheric temperature; and the much greater increase due to physical work. The execution of this rarely skilled investigator at the age of 51 was one of the major tragedies of the French Revolution.

Thus, what we may consider as the basic physical aspects of metabolism, its relation to respiration and to the elimination of heat, were worked out in France at the end of the eighteenth century. The aspects of the subject relating to the problems of organic chemistry involved were elucidated by the German school of physiologists under the leadership of Liebig in the middle of the early nineteenth century. T. Schwann introduced the term "metabolic phenomena" in 1839; and Justus von Liebig, in 1842, published a full analysis of the concept of metabolism.[72] He sums up the whole problem in one sentence: "The reaction between the constituents of food and oxygen circulating through the body in the blood is the source of animal heat."

Five years later, H. von Helmholtz announced the general

principle of the conservation of energy, into which metabolism fits as a special case.

Measurement of Metabolism

The actual large-scale quantitative study of metabolism along the lines laid down by Liebig was begun at Munich by Voit and Pettenkofer in the sixties and seventies, and continued at Berlin by Rubner in the later nineteenth century. In America, W. O. Atwater and F. G. Benedict perfected the equipment of apparatus for calorimetric study, and the latter investigator has continued his distinguished leadership up to the present day.

The quantitative measurement of metabolism can be accomplished in two ways. The most obvious method is to enclose the individual in a chamber so constructed as to measure the heat contributed by the subject to the chamber and its atmosphere. This is called "direct calorimetry." A second method, known as "indirect calorimetry" has wider application and depends on the computation of the heat produced from the decrease in oxygen and the increase in carbon dioxide due to respiration. The latter procedure was introduced nearly a century ago (in 1849) by Reignault and Reiset in France. They observed animals in a closed gaseous circuit and noted the "respiratory quotient, the ratio of the volume of carbon dioxide expired divided by that of the oxygen inspired. In a fasting individual, this quotient is a little over .7; after consumption of a high-protein diet, the quotient falls, since much of the oxygen is utilized in oxidizing the nitrogenous part of the food molecule."

As an illustration of the procedure, we may quote from DuBois's description of his calorimeter in the New York Hospital.[27] This apparatus is a large copper box with a front consisting of two glass plates sealed by wax. The subject lies in a string net hammock, suspended in a wooden frame, to eliminate direct conduction to solid surfaces. For indirect calorimetry, a current of air is drawn through the chamber, and, on the exit side, this air is passed through sulphuric acid bottles to collect the water given off by evaporation from the subject, then through a bottle of soda lime to absorb the carbon dioxide produced, and finally through a second sulphuric acid bottle to take up moisture which has been absorbed from the soda lime. As oxygen is consumed from the air circuit, it is automatically replaced from a weighed cylinder. From the oxygen consumed and the carbon dioxide given off by the subject, the metabolism is computed.

For direct calorimetry, the actual heat given off to the chamber by the subject is recorded. The chamber has a double copper wall and both walls are kept at exactly the same temperature so that no heat can be lost from the inner wall of the chamber itself. The outgoing air is maintained at the same temperature as the incoming air by the cooling effect of a coil of water pipes in the ceiling, and the amount of heat eliminated is computed from the temperature of the water entering and leaving the coils. The total weight of water vaporized is determined by measuring the moisture in the air through absorption in sulphuric acid. The heat given off to the coils plus the heat of vaporization of the water gives the total metabolism. The results of indirect and direct calorimetry check each other closely (within 2 to 3 per cent).

Basal Metabolism

The height of metabolic activity varies with the size and body-build of the individual, with age and sex, and possibly to some extent with race. In a given individual, at a given age, it varies enormously with the degree of muscular work performed. It may vary to a less marked degree with the temperature of the environment; and with the activity of digestive processes which involve oxidations after a meal, metabolism may increase by 5 to 30 per cent, a phenomenon labeled as due to the "specific dynamic action" of foodstuffs, and not completely understood.

To eliminate these variables, physiologists have introduced

the concept of "basal metabolism." This is the level of metabolic activity displayed by a subject at rest at an air temperature of about 70°F and at a period long enough after a meal to avoid the specific dynamic action of food. This value is remarkably constant. For an individual of average weight and body build, it will be roughly of the order of 60 calories per hour, of which about one-fourth is believed to be due to work done by the involuntary muscles of the circulatory and respiratory systems, and the rest in part to muscle tonus and in part to oxidation changes in the tissues. Here, and in all our following discussion, we are dealing with the "large calorie," the amount of heat necessary to raise the temperature of 1 kilogram of water by 1°C, since this is the unit ordinarily employed by physiologists.

As to actual metabolic levels, Atwater and Benedict reported a figure of 2280 calories per 24-hours for the quiet life of young men in a calorimetric chamber. Lusk cites a figure of 1840 calories per 24-hours under conditions of absolute bed-rest with food, and of 1680 calories for bed-rest without food. Benedict and Carpenter observed a rate as low as 1500 calories per 24-hours during sleep.

Relation of Metabolism to the Surface Area of the Body

As early as 1849 Reignault and Reiset investigated the metabolic rates of various species of birds and drew the following very significant conclusions: "The consumption of oxygen absorbed varies greatly in different animals per unit of body weight. It is ten times greater in sparrows than in chickens. Since the different species have the same body temperature, and the smaller animals present a relatively larger area to the environmental air, they experience a substantial cooling effect, and it becomes necessary that the sources of heat production operate more energetically and that respiration increase." The hypothesis that metabolism was primarily related to surface area was elaborated by Rubner and Richet in 1883. Rubner studied a series of dogs varying in weight from 3.1 kilograms to 30.7 kilograms and in metabolic activity from 273 to 1124 calories, and found that the metabolic rate per square meter of body surface varied only from 1046 to 1214 calories. Lusk cites the following very striking figures for various animal species.

	Weight, kg.	Metabolism, calories per sq. meter per day
Hog	128	1074
Man	64	1042
Dog	15	1039
Guinea pig	0.5	1246
Mouse	0.018	1183

Deviations in other animal species are somewhat greater than those cited. Benedict and his associates find that, for large mammals, resting metabolism per square meter is higher, ranging around 1500 to 1600 calories for the horse and the steer, and around 1700 calories for the elephant. It seems not at all unreasonable to suppose that the rate of metabolic activity may have been developed in the course of evolution at a level which would permit the maintenance of the temperature of the tissues during sleep with a rate of heat loss determined by the surface area of the body.

Missenard [80] cites experiments of Giaja indicating that in several species of birds there may be a lowering of metabolism below basal values due to some form of chemical regulation in an atmosphere above the optimal temperature; but this is not a regular effect in man, although DuBois has noted a moderate decrease in women under warm conditions.

Missenard tabulates results of various observers on rates of assumed basal metabolism for 31 different species of birds and mammals. The results for 24 species fall within a range not too remote from those observed in man. Eight species showed a metabolic rate between 30 and 40 calories per square meter per hour; 8 species were between 40 and 50 calories; and 6 were between 50 and 60 calories per hour. Results for 5 species, the mouse, the mole, the hedgehog, the goat, and the eagle, were, however, below 30 calories (22 in the case of the mouse); while 4 species, the elephant, the turkey, the swallow, and the goldfinch, were above 60 calories (68 in the case of the swallow and 86 in the case of the elephant). Three of the species with low rates are small, and two of the species with high rates are large; there is obviously no direct relation to size. The state of truly basal metabolism with various species of animals is very difficult to define. It is significant that in spite of such differences the white mouse weighing 34 grams and the elephant weighing 3700 kilograms show metabolic rates varying only from 36 to 86 calories per square meter of body surface per hour.

In human beings there seems no doubt of the validity of the surface area law, and metabolism is most accurately computed in terms of calories per square meter. The measurement of this area presents complications, but the problem has been solved with reasonable accuracy by methods described by DuBois. He has suggested the following formula for its approximate estimation:

$$\text{Area (sq.cm.)} = \text{Weight (kg.)}^{.425} \times \text{Height (cm.)}^{.725} \times 71.84.$$

A table based on this formula indicates variations from 0.91 square meter to 2.41 square meters for men of various sizes and body builds.

Sherman[115] cites a considerable series of observations on various human subjects, all falling within 10 per cent of a basal metabolism of 39.7 calories per square meter per hour. Since the center of metabolic activity is in the protoplasm of the active tissues of the body, a fat man with a larger percentage of inactive adipose tissue shows values slightly below the mean; women show a 5 per cent lower metabolism than men for the same reason. On the other hand, Benedict found that the trained athlete has a metabolism about 5 per cent above the mean. In both sexes the detailed standards worked out by the Mayo Foundation show a generally progressive fall with age, presumably related to the relative proportion of active vital tissue in the body. For males the mean basal metabolism, according to these tables, falls rather rapidly from over 50 calories per square meter in children under 8 years of age, to about 40 calories at the age of twenty-five, and then decreases more slowly to about 36 calories at the age of sixty.

The following table given by DuBois well indicates the major influences of sex and age.

Age in years	Metabolism per sq. meter	Calories per hr.
	Male	*Female*
14–16	46.0	43.0
70–80	35.5	33.0

Whether significant differences in metabolic activity are associated with race remains a debatable question.

The Influence of Muscular Work upon Metabolism

The figures just cited refer to basal metabolism, which is a somewhat artificial experimental condition. The main factor which alters metabolic activity is muscular work; and differences due to this cause far overshadow minor differences in the basal level. As an illustration we may take an experiment made in our own laboratory. Two subjects were studied, one with a surface area of 1.92 square meters, the other with a surface area of 1.81 square meters. The metabolism of these two subjects averaged 45.6 calories per square meter or 84.8 calories per man when seated at rest in the calorimetric chamber, a value no doubt somewhat above the basal level. In the experiments here discussed, the subjects worked on a stationary bicycle (a posture involving, even at rest, considerable muscular adjustment, and therefore again raising the metabolic level). They pedaled the bicycle at a constant rate of 38 revolutions per minute against a varying load requiring various amounts of work.[131] The table below represents the averages of a series of tests on the two subjects. Calories per man are compared in this case, rather than calories per square meter. The work done is expressed in terms of equivalent calories, one foot-pound equaling .31 calorie.

Work done, in equivalent of calories/hour	Work done, excess over minimum rate	Metabolism, calories/man per hour	Metabolism, excess over minimum rate	Per cent efficiency
8		169		
19	11	201	32	34
45	37	302	133	28
57	49	384	215	23
70	62	423	254	24

It will be noted that the increase in work performed is directly reflected in a corresponding increase in metabolism, and that the rise in metabolism (except in the first increase from 8 to 19 calories of work performed where the figures are too small for accuracy) is approximately 25 per cent of the parallel increase in work performed. Earlier work by Benedict and his associates gave efficiencies varying from 13 to 22 per cent; but more recent studies, as summarized by DuBois, indicate 20 to 30 per cent as a probable figure.

Sherman[115] gives the estimate (page 21) of metabolic rates for a man of average stature and weight.

Even higher rates than those cited may be attained for short periods of time; but they quickly result in exhaustion. Three classical experiments along this line may be cited, in which careful records were made of work performed under extreme conditions.

Benedict and Cathcart observed a professional bicycle rider working to the point of exhaustion on a bicycle ergometer. He was unable to continue after 4 hours and 22 minutes; and during this period he worked at a rate of 111.6 kilogram-calories per hour. The metabolism of the subject was not actually observed; but the excess over basal metabolism was computed from the work performed, assuming an efficiency of 25 per cent. During the period of activity the subject accomplished work at the rate of 112 calories per hour, giving a computed total metabolism of 526 calories per hour, approximately Sherman's estimate for swimming.[11] Henderson and Haggard [53] recorded the work performed in a crew race in which exhaustion occurred after 22 minutes. Here the work performed was at the rate of 288 calories per hour. Assuming a 25 per cent efficiency, this indicates a work-metabolism rate of 1152 calories per hour, plus an estimated basal metabolism of 80, a total of 1230 calories per hour.

Occupation	Calories per man per hour
Sleeping	65
Sitting at rest	100
Typewriting rapidly	140
Walking at 2.60 miles per hour	200
Walking at 3.75 miles per hour	300
Stone working	400
Swimming	500
Walking up a flight of stairs	1100

Finally, Nielsen,[97] actually recorded the metabolism of a subject working on an ergometer under such extreme conditions that the subject was completely exhausted in 22 seconds. (For the student of Numerology, it may be noted that the presence of the number 22 in these three studies is purely coincidental.) Nielsen's subject showed a metabolic rate during his 22 seconds of 3930 calories per hour.

From these three studies we derive the following relationships:

	Period of exhaustion, hours	Metabolism, calories per hour
Benedict	4.367	526
Henderson	0.367	1230
Nielsen	0.006	3930

Comparing Benedict and Henderson, an approximate doubling of metabolic rate decreased the time limit to about one-twelfth of its Benedict value. Comparing Henderson and Nielsen, a further tripling of metabolic rate decreased the period of endurance to one-sixtieth of the Henderson figure.

Thus we see that enormous rates of metabolism can be maintained for brief periods of time. Computations on an hourly basis are, however, obviously artificial. Only some figure between 500 and 1000 calories could actually be maintained for as long as one hour. On a 24-hour basis, it has been estimated that trained participants in a 6-day bicycle race might maintain a rate of some 10,000 calories per day. Under ordinary circumstances the metabolism of a 24-hour period with average muscular work has been computed by Sherman as follows:

	CALORIES
8 hours sleep at 65 calories per hour	520
6 hours sitting at rest at 100 calories per hour	600
2 hours light exercise at 170 calories per hour	340
8 hours carpenter work at 240 calories per hour	1920
	3380

If we substitute a heavier task such as stone working (400 calories per hour) under the 8-hour work period, the total would be increased to 4660 calories per 24 hours. The daily extremes for various forms of normal human activity will vary between 2000 and 5000 calories.

Studies of considerable interest with respect to the relation between food energy and work accomplished were made in Germany during the war. Kraut and Muller[69] showed the remarkably close relation between factory work performed and the calorie intake of the diet in excess of a basal figure. This excess was designated as "work calories," with a constant weight. When the diet was reduced the amount of work performed fell off, or in cases of special psychological stimulation, there was a weight loss. A most striking graph shows the relation between coal production in the Ruhr and calorie consumption, the amount of work performed stabilizing itself at a figure of about 1200 work calories per ton of coal output.

Influence of Environmental Temperature upon Metabolism

Within a range of atmospheric conditions, within and slightly above the comfort range, metabolism remains unaffected. Beyond this range metabolic rates tend to increase on each side, for quite different reasons. The initial stages of this phenomenon are illustrated by an analysis of the following data obtained in our laboratory.[38, 139]

In one series of experiments 35 tests were made on each of two subjects, at varying operative temperatures from 18°C up to 41°C. (The operative temperature represents the combined effect of air and wall temperatures, and will be discussed in a later chapter.) Air and walls were nearly identical; under these circumstances, operative temperature is, of course, the same as the air temperature.

In another study, 44 experiments were made on clothed and on nude subjects, with a somewhat similar variation in air temperatures, and, again, with walls at the same temperature as the air. In the table below, we have averaged the observed metabolic rate (per square meter of body surface) as observed in three major ranges of environmental temperature.

No experiments were performed with the nude subjects below 20°C. In the case of Subject No. 1 in Study A, the value of 42 under cold conditions was clearly unreliable, since there were only two experiments in this temperature range and one of them showed a quite abnormally low metabolism. Subject No. 2, in Study A, and the clothed subjects in Study B, showed a marked and significant rise in metabolic rate under the cold conditions.

Operative temperature	Mean metabolism per square meter cal./m.^{2}/hr.		
	Under 20°C	20° to 24.9°C	Over 24.9°C
Study A, mean, Subject 1	42	44	46
Study A, mean, Subject 2	56	49	51
Study B, mean, clothed subjects	53	49	49
Study B, mean, nude subjects		47	49

On the other hand, the hot conditions in all cases but that of the clothed subjects of Study B show a slight but appreciable increase in metabolism.

It appears that, in general, the minimum metabolism is observed at 20° to 25°C and that below 20° and above 25°C there is a tendency to increased metabolic rate.

The increase under cold conditions is clearly a useful adaptive reaction. There has been much discussion as to how this is brought about and whether there is any mechanism of chemical regulation by which such an adaptation can be effected. Under extreme conditions shivering sets in, which involves muscular activity and provides a physical explanation for the phenomenon. It seems probable that in less extreme chilling (such as obtained in our experiments, where no shivering occurred) there is a tensing of the muscles. There seems no reason to assume that other or less familiar processes are involved.

The increase in metabolism above the comfort zone is clearly not an adaptive process, but the reverse. It is apparently due to a direct stimulation of tissue oxidation due to increased body temperature. The phenomenon of heat stroke (common in the boiler room of vessels in the early days of steam transport) shows how dangerous such a process may be. Under extreme conditions of heat, the warming up of the body tissues was accompanied by an increase in metabolism, which, in turn, accentuated heating up. The body temperature rose to 105°–110°F and death promptly ensued.

Metabolism in Fever

In general, the human body has adaptive mechanisms, to be discussed in Chapter III, which enable it to cope with environmental conditions, unless they reach the extreme conditions of heat stroke just discussed. The phenomenon of fever, which has been studied in particular by DuBois, represents a failure of this adaptive mechanism.

Under the influences of certain toxic substances, such as those produced by infecting microbes or by the injection of certain foreign proteins, the body temperature rises sharply, and DuBois finds that this is due to an increase in heat production without a corresponding rise in heat elimination. When metabolism rises with exercise, heat elimination rises also, and the rise of body temperature is relatively slight. DuBois observed, in the course of a malarial chill, an increase of metabolism from 80 to 230 calories per square meter per hour with no corresponding rise in heat loss. The temperature of the skin under such a condition commonly falls (which, of course, tends to decrease loss and accounts for the chilling sensation), and sweat secretion does not rise as it does in the normal person during exercise. Hence, the temperature of the body tissues must increase, although it is a strange fact that the process is apparently self-limited, the body temperature very rarely rising over 105°.[27] The initial fall in skin temperature is due to sharp vasoconstriction of skin vessels. This fall is temporary and due to the fact that a considerable thermal insulation has suddenly been placed in the path of a balanced heat flow from internal regions to the skin surface. This effect is similar to that produced by a radiator thermostat in an automobile. By closing on a cold morning, such a thermostat prevents engine water from reaching the radiator. The radiator (skin) cools, and engine temperature (internal body region) rises. In the case of fever the total rise of internal temperature is a compound effect of this increased thermal insulation of a constricted skin circulation and large increases in actual heat production. The whole phenomenon is an obscure and intriguing one. It is clear, however, that it involves a disturbance of the coordinating machinery which the body has developed for the regulation of temperature.

The Practical Problem of Human Comfort

The problem presented to the hygienist in the fields of clothing and air conditioning is largely determined by the data which have been presented in this chapter.

The human organism, in the conduct of normal life processes, produces an amount of heat which, aside from exceptional conditions, involves the production of from 100 to 1000 calories per hour. This heat must be eliminated at approximately the same rate at which it is produced, if the temperature of the body tissues is not to fall or to rise beyond the level compatible with comfort, efficiency, or even life itself.

How this heat is dissipated, what adaptive mechanisms the body has to facilitate its elimination, and how the hygienist can assist in the process will be the subjects of succeeding chapters.

~~~~~~

AVENUES OF HEAT LOSS FROM
THE BODY

Heat Losses from the Body

PRACTICAL knowledge of the influence of environmental temperature upon the human body goes far back of the earliest records of scientific thought. In the third chapter of Genesis, Adam and Eve heard the voice of God as they were "walking in the garden in the cool of the day."

Whatever psychological factors may have been at work in the Garden of Eden, it is probable that our most primitive ancestors adopted the use of clothing in cold climates, partly as a means of protection against the chilling effect of the atmosphere; and the heating power of the sun's rays must have been one of the earliest facts which impressed itself on dawning human consciousness. The cooling effect of evaporation was probably a much later conception. Its real significance as expressed in the common phrase, "it isn't the heat, it's the humidity," is probably not really understood by most people who use the phrase today. Yet the truth that three different factors, convection, radiation, and evaporation, influence thermal comfort is implicit in everyday knowledge and practice, and was recognized by physiologists as soon as the basic concepts of physics began to influence those of biology. Rubner, in 1896, estimated that under what may be considered as average atmospheric conditions, 44 per cent of body heat is lost by radiation to cold surfaces surrounding the body, 32 per cent by convection loss to the air from the skin, and mucous

27

surfaces of nose and throat, 21 per cent by evaporation from the skin and the mucous surfaces, and the remaining 3 per cent by work done and the warming of ingested food.

Taking "convection" first, we may draw attention to the fact that in physiological studies of human heat loss, this term usually covers the rather large fraction of heat carried away from the body by moving air, and also a smaller heat loss which takes place from the body surface to the environment by direct contact between skin and external surfaces. This latter contact heat loss is really conduction, a physical heat transfer process which is distinct from convection. In conducted heat loss, the heat transfer passes the surface of contact by a transmittal of molecular heat vibrations without any physical transfer of material. In convected heat loss, on the other hand, a physical material such as air or water circulates over the heated surface and effects the heat transfer by becoming elevated in temperature and moving away to be replaced by cooler fluid which continues the process.

Since the human body under practical circumstances is usually separated from solid objects in the environment by clothing, which is a poor contact or conduction heat-transfer material, the simplified analysis of human heat transfer has usually restricted itself to the three processes, radiation, evaporation, and convection. The small conducted heat losses are either neglected, or, due to the method of accounting for total heat loss by progressive subtraction of measured radiation, evaporation, and convection losses, the element of pure conduction loss is contained in the convection fraction, and is not separately analyzed.

Under certain conditions, however, conducted heat loss may be important for human comfort, and since much of our experience with "heat" and "cold" is gained from incidental skin contacts with solid objects of varying temperatures and heat conductive power, a few examples of heat conduction as distinct from convection may be given.

We have all experienced the sensation of sitting on a cold

stone bench in winter, and have probably noticed that an adjacent wooden bench "felt" warmer although the actual temperatures of the benches were not different. A hot rock exposed to the sun is likewise apparently "warmer" than a wooden surface at the same temperature. Solids vary widely in their power of conducting heat. DuBois reminds us that "Silver is an excellent conductor, as we realize when a silver spoon is put into a plate of hot soup. Glass is a very poor conductor and cork is one of the poorest of all, and therefore, one of the best insulators." He points out that "if you walk barefoot into a bathroom and step on a rug, it feels warmer than the tile floor which is uncomfortably cold. Reason tells you that the two are exactly the same temperature, since they have been exposed to the same air conditions all night. The rug, which is a poor conductor, abstracts very little heat from the skin and causes little or no change in skin temperature; the tiled floor withdraws heat rapidly and cools the soles of the feet in a fraction of a second."

Hardy has abstracted from physical handbooks a few representative thermal conductivity values for materials which, in ordinary experience, give us our impression of conductivity as distinct from temperature.

	gm. cals./cm.^{2}/cm./sec./°C
Silver	0.99
Glass	0.0025
Softwood	0.00009
Leather (tanned)	0.0004
Paper	0.0003
Cotton Wool	0.0004
Air	0.000057

As can be readily seen from this table,[48] silver exceeds air in ability to conduct heat by a factor of 18,000 to 1. In the selection of flooring surfaces and in the design of seating equipment and of instrument and utensil handles, these differences are important to human comfort.

In any practical consideration of the problems of air conditioning, however, this factor of solid or liquid conduction may be omitted from consideration, and is reduced to a negligible minimum (as pointed out in Chapter I) in physiological experimentation. Our interest lies primarily in heat loss to the surrounding atmosphere. Such heat loss is, strictly speaking, transfer of heat from the body surfaces to the air in direct contact with such surfaces; but the air is in constant motion either as a result of temperature currents or wind movement. So that fresh cooler air continually replaces that warmed by the body. The total process is, therefore, called cooling by convection rather than by conduction. Two or three per cent of heat loss of this type is due to the warming of the respired air and the rest to heat loss from the skin, but for practical purposes these need not be separated. It should of course be remembered that convection may be either a cooling or a heating process, depending on whether the air is below or above the mean temperature of the body surface.

Evaporation, on the other hand, is always a cooling factor. It is generally estimated that the evaporation of one gram of water requires the application of .58 calorie of heat (although Murlin and Burton,[91] as well as Hardy,[48] have pointed out that this value applies only to the vaporization of water at 22°C, and at other temperatures of skin and air the value may vary from .58 to .66). Hence, every gram of water actually evaporated from the surface of the skin or of the mucous membranes will cool the body by a certain amount. Under average atmospheric conditions, with a subject at rest, this avenue of heat loss accounts for one-fifth to one-fourth of the total heat loss from the body, nearly half of which may be contributed by evaporation from the nose and throat.

Curiously enough, the factor of radiation is the one which has been most neglected in physiological thinking until recent times. The effect of the sun or of an open fire has been recognized; but it has been largely forgotten that at all times and in all circumstances there is an exchange of heat between surfaces of different temperature by direct passage of infrared heat rays, without reference to the temperature of the intervening atmosphere. The human body constantly loses heat by this process to all surfaces cooler than itself and constantly gains heat from all surfaces warmer than itself.

Almost everyone has had practical experience with an inconspicuous but important and common radiation effect on comfort. In the early Autumn when outside temperatures are only 5° to 7°C below a comfortable inside temperature, an air thermostat set for 21°C air temperature produces a very satisfactory condition. Under these conditions, the outer walls of the house, which exchange radiation with our body surface, are very near 21°C, and it is correct to say that we are exposed to a radiation and a convection air temperature which approximates 21°C. However, when outside temperatures fall to 5°, air temperatures 1° to 2°C higher are required for similar comfort. The exposed walls may be as low as 18°C, some 1° to 3° below air temperature. Under such circumstances the walls exert a greater direct cooling effect than was the case when they were at 21°C, and we raise our air temperatures to compensate for this effect.

Pettenkofer, seventy years ago, had a clear understanding of the importance of this radiative factor of heat loss. In his *Populäre Vorträge,* he says: "We must consider ourselves as warm and moist bodies surrounded by a cooler atmosphere. Such bodies lose heat in three ways: (1) by Radiation; (2) by Evaporation; (3) by Conduction. The fact that the heat is dissipated, not by one pathway but by three, provides material advantages in the maintenance of body temperature, in the heat economy of the body, since the use of three channels permits a delicate regulation of the heat loss, according to needs." He illustrates the importance of the factor of radiation by comparing the sensations of a traveler in a room at an inn in which a fire has just been lighted, who suffers from cold (due to radiation to cold walls) at an air temperature of 16°; while two days later (after the walls have been warmed up) he is quite comfortable at 14°. He also cites the sensation of over-heating experienced in a crowded room as a result of radiation from the bodies of the occupants.[103]

The importance of radiation was, as we have seen, recognized by Rubner in 1896; but this avenue of heat loss was more or less completely ignored in the early years of the present century. Benedict and Carpenter, and the pioneer investigators at the Laboratory of the American Society of Heating and Ventilating Engineers in Pittsburgh studied the heat loss by radiation and convection as a combined single factor. This can be done, of course, if air and surrounding surfaces are all at essentially the same temperature. Aldrich, in 1928, was the first observer in this country to determine radiation heat loss with accuracy.[1] It was Bohnenkamp in Germany who, in 1931, really developed the subject in an exhaustive manner.[13] He emphasized the fact that radiation heat loss is governed not by total body surface area but by the area actually exposed to radiation interchange with surrounding surfaces. He determined this factor by photographic measurements of the areas "seen" by the camera from various angles. He then proceeded to direct measurement of the heat radiated from various areas of the skin surface. He demonstrated the conformity of radiation interchange with the physical laws of Stefan and Boltzmann, and showed that this factor in bodily heat loss might be very large, as much as 70 per cent of total metabolism. Bohnenkamp, however, estimated both evaporative and convective effects, as earlier observers had estimated (or ignored) radiative effects. His pioneer observations on radiation were continued by Hardy, DuBois, and Burton in this country, and the admirable radiometer devised by Hardy greatly facilitated progress.

So far as thermal exchanges between the body and its surroundings are concerned, there are, then, four major factors. The human body in a state of equilibrium with its thermal environment produces heat by metabolism. It loses heat by evaporation. It loses or gains heat by convection and radiation, depending on the environmental conditions. The whole closed system, when equilibrium exists, may be expressed by the simple formula:

$$M \text{ (metabolism)} - E \text{ (evaporation)} \pm C \text{ (convection)} \pm R \text{ (radiation)} = 0$$

States of disequilibrium or temporarily imperfect adjustment often exist and, in some respects, may be of greater assistance in understanding the problem than the condition of full thermal adaptation. In such states the right side of the equation is not zero but has a positive or negative value, representing actual chilling or heating of body tissues. This subject will be discussed later.

Partitional Calorimetry

In 1936 the authors, with the collaboration of A. P. Gagge, initiated a systematic approach to the whole problem by the introduction of a method designated as "Partitional Calorimetry."[137] The advantages (and the limitations) of this procedure were described as follows:

"We present here a new method of calorimetry which seems peculiarly adapted for the study of body heat elimination and temperature regulation. From a theoretical standpoint its chief characteristics, as contrasted with the use of static or "heat trap" calorimeters, are two. In the first place, it makes possible a record of thermal interchanges as they occur *within a brief interval of time* instead of summing up results extending over a period of several hours, in which the process of adaptation is masked by cumulative averages. In the second place, its data are given in terms of rates of thermal interchange partitioned by primary measurement in accordance with the physical avenues through which the interchanges occur.

"For the procedure in question, we employ the term *partitional calorimetry* to distinguish it clearly from the conventional form of static calorimetry in which the primary measurement consists of a quantity of heat 'captured' by the apparatus.

"Direct Calorimetry of the ordinary type is not adapted to a study of the biophysics of heat elimination when experimental interest demands an accurate partition of the energy metabolism. This arises from the fact that the direct calorimeter affords no convenient method for the separate determination of the values of radiation and convection loss. In addition, the temperature range over which such apparatus can operate is limited, in practice if not in theory, by the labor involved in determining the constants of a calorimeter for more than one condition. Furthermore, long-time observations in an ordinary calorimeter can only be conducted under conditions within a fairly narrow range of physiological adaptability; while for the shorter periods required by our procedure, the subject can endure more extreme ranges of heat and cold.

"A generalized biophysical treatment of the problem would not be greatly furthered even by a complete and accurate partition under a single standard environmental condition. Such a generalized treatment of the problem can be furthered only by empirical partitions over a wide range of conditions, incorporated in a methodological framework which permits the derivation of the equational forms and constants necessary for a general solution. In the briefest possible terms, the end which we have sought is the determination of the several functional relations which will make possible the computation of the 'probable calorie demand' of a given physical environment upon an organism of any given physical and thermogenic proportions, and the partition of that demand between the various avenues of heat loss."

To carry out such a study it was essential to design an apparatus in which the various environmental conditions (air temperature, air movement, atmospheric humidity, and mean radiant temperature) could be accurately controlled and varied independently. For this purpose a nine-paneled booth of copper was constructed (as illustrated in Figures 1 and 2). The air supplied to this booth and to the room in which it was located, was regulated as to temperature and humidity by the usual engineering procedures. Air temperature within the booth could be varied from 5° to 60°C and relative humidity from 15 to 95 per cent of saturation. The air was introduced

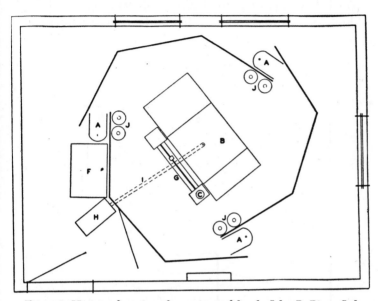

Figure 1. Horizontal section of experimental booth, John B. Pierce Laboratory, New Haven, Conn. Equipment for study of thermal interchanges by the method of partitional calorimetry. *A*, 2500-watt heaters; *B*, chair; *C*, aspirating psychrometer; *D*, Moll thermopile; *E*, copper hemisphere (radiometer); *F*, chart table; *G*, platform scales (balancing beam in Figure 1, platform in Figure 2); *H*, Benedict-Roth metabolism apparatus; *I*, hose connection to metabolism apparatus; *J*, six-inch fans directed to floor of booth; *K*, reference temperature bath for rectal thermocouple.

so that the velocity was minimal (15 to 25 feet per minute). Higher velocities could be produced at will by the use of small fans located near the top of the booth. The new feature of the apparatus was the heating of the chamber by reflection from the copper surfaces of infrared radiant heat directed against the interior of the walls by electrical heating elements located at openings between the three three-panel elements of the wall. Since copper reflects some 98 per cent of the infrared radiation which it receives, the subject seated within the booth received the full effect of hot radiation from the wall surfaces while those surfaces themselves remained at approximately air temperature, so that convection currents due to hot walls were avoided. It was possible to obtain an air temperature of 5°C within the enclosure and to maintain the contact temperature of the walls at close to that figure, while these same walls were

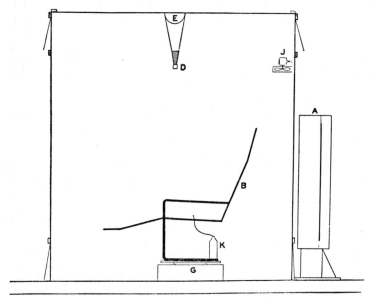

Figure 2. Vertical section of experimental booth, John B. Pierce Laboratory, New Haven, Conn. See legend of Figure 1.

reflecting radiant heat equivalent to that which would be given off by walls at 45°C. This situation was, of course, essential to the successful separation of radiative and convective effects; and it was a most unusual experience to sit in the booth and feel the waves of heat coming from the surrounding surfaces and then to place one's hand on these surfaces and find them extremely cold to the touch.

With an apparatus of this kind it was possible to vary each factor in thermal interchange between the body and its environment and to deduce the quantitative effect of variation in air temperature, or air movement, or radiative heating, with all other factors kept constant. This was first done for each factor in a state of equilibrium (as indicated by relative constancy in skin temperature and rectal temperature). Metabolism and evaporation were recorded directly, and convective and radiative factors computed from the difference between mean skin temperature and mean air temperature, or mean skin temperature and mean radiative temperature, according to the relations derived from a study of convection or radiation as the only independent variable. Having done this for equilibrium states, it was possible to proceed to states of disequilibrium and to determine changes in temperature of the body tissues themselves (positive or negative values of the right side of the previous equation relating M, E, R, and C) by difference.

Our earlier studies were all made with nude subjects seated in the chair indicated in Figure 2. Each experiment covered a period of about three hours, so that it was possible to make many tests with different subjects, and to cover a vastly wider range of conditions than would be feasible in the use of a calorimeter of the usual type. The work of Houghton and his associates at Pittsburgh[62] is the only study which has had similar scope, and in that study effects due to convection and radiation were not separated.

Measurement of Metabolism and Evaporation

These two factors were determined directly in each experiment.

Metabolic rate was recorded by two observations made at about one hour and two hours after the initiation of the experiment. The determination was made by the use of the Benedict-Roth apparatus, on the principle discussed in Chapter I, the consumption of oxygen giving the measure of metabolic activity. The experiments were not conducted under strictly basal conditions but under conditions which were standard within themselves. Breakfast and luncheon of moderate proportions were allowed at a period before morning and afternoon experiments, but active exercise was prohibited. The metabolic levels attained were, therefore, slightly above basal figures. Thirty-five different experiments with a stout subject gave a mean of 45 calories per square meter, with a low value of 41 and a high of 50. Thirty-five experiments with a slender subject gave a mean of 51 calories per square meter, with extreme values of 44 and 58. Even with this more variable subject, only four experiments showed figures deviating by more than 10 per cent from the mean. In experiments involving the performance of work equivalent to 70 kilogram-calories (on a stationary bicycle), metabolic rates rose to between 220 and 260 kilogram-calories.

Evaporative heat loss was computed from direct observations of weight loss. The chair on which the subject sat rested on a platform scale with a sensitivity of 2 grams. Readings of this scale were made at 20-minute intervals during the experiment, and weight loss was transferred into calories of evaporative cooling by subtracting the weight inequalities due to substitution of carbon dioxide for oxygen in the expired air (derived from the observed consumption of oxygen), and allowing 0.58 calorie of heat loss for each gram of water actually evaporated. It should be noted, of course, that only moisture actually evaporated from the surface of skin or clothing (and that eliminated in the expired air) exerts a cooling effect upon the body. If sweat runs off in drops, it does not accomplish its cooling function, as will be indicated in a later paragraph.

In one series of 70 experiments with two different subjects, with atmospheric relative humidities of about 50 per cent, and air and wall temperatures varying over a wide range, we found that under cool conditions (about 20°C) evaporative heat loss was 11 to 12 calories per square meter; but at high temperatures (about 35°C) the value rose to 90 calories per square meter, about double the metabolic rate of heat production.

Measurement of Heat Loss by Radiation

Heat loss (or gain) by radiation, unlike the heat gain due to metabolism and the heat loss due to evaporation, cannot be recorded directly; but the methods of partitional calorimetry have made it possible to measure it with a high degree of accuracy. It is obvious that heat exchange of this type depends upon four factors: one of these factors is associated with the environment: (1) the mean radiant temperature (infrared) of surrounding environmental surfaces as influenced by (a) the emissivity of these surfaces, and (b) the intensity of radiation sources. The remaining three factors are associated with the human body, and are (2) the mean temperature of the external surfaces of the body, (3) the surface area of the body which is effective in radiation interchange, and (4) the radiation absorption characteristics of the body surfaces. Human skin and ordinary clothing have 98+ per cent absorptive and emissive properties for infrared heat rays, and (in the absence of polished surfaces) the emissivity of most interior environments is above 95 per cent, hence under average indoor circumstances the values for the emissivity factors (1a) and (4) may be considered unity, and the remaining factors regarded as the important variables.

In the range of visible light, the human skin does not behave as a black body. The white skin absorbs 60 to 70 per cent of sunlight and the negro skin about 82 per cent. For analysis of the ordinary conditions of life, however, in which the infrared rays are the ones which are effective, absorption of heat radiation may be considered as complete. It is helpful, in considering this different reflective power of skin and other surfaces for different wave lengths, to keep in mind that the temperature of the source producing the radiation is the most important factor in determining the character of radiation. The sun, with a temperature of 6000°C, is the typical source of radiation in the near infrared and visible spectrum for which, as noted above, the skin is only a partial reflector. No other source of radiation with which we are in usual contact even approaches this temperature, and, in fact, most of our heat exchange is with surfaces below 100°C, where the long infrared radiation is predominant. It is this range of wave length which is important from the standpoint of heat interchange.

In the partitional calorimeter, the mean radiant temperature of the environment was measured, in our experiments, by a Moll 80-element thermopile, whose optical field was the surface of a 6-inch copper hemisphere suspended from the ceiling of the booth. The reading of the pile, when properly calibrated[132] gave an accurate picture of the mean radiant effects involved. The surface temperature of the body was recorded by a Hardy thermopile[47] at fifteen different circular areas of 1.5 inches diameter; three on the head, three on the upper extremities, four on the trunk, and five on the lower extremities. Both Murlin[90] and Hardy have discussed at length the technical precautions necessary in order to make this measurement with minimum error.

The effective radiation surface of the body was the factor which remained to be determined. To obtain this factor, we conducted a series of experiments in which convection loss was held constant by maintaining a constant difference between air temperature and skin temperature. Metabolism and evaporation were directly observed, and change in body temperature was recorded by a rectal thermometer. Radiative conditions were varied over a wide range.

We then plotted radiation intensity against the observed figure for metabolism minus evaporation, plus-or-minus any recorded change in body heat, as indicated in Figure 3.

It will be noted that observations made in the central areas of each graph lie close to a definite trend line, while with very low and very high radiative intensity, they lie to the left of the trend line. Deviations with very low intensity (at the left of the graph) indicate that the measurement of rectal temperature did not accurately record changes in average body temperature for these extreme conditions, with body tissues cooling very rapidly. Deviations with very high radiative intensity, in two of the graphs, indicate that sweat was running off without exerting its assumed cooling influence. In the region where

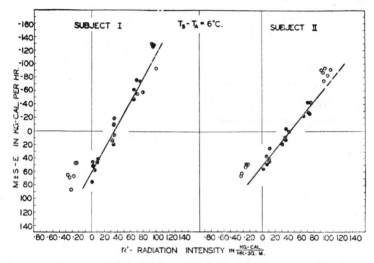

Figure 3. Relation of heat balance to radiation intensity.

observations follow the trend line, it may be demonstrated on the basis of what Gagge[33] termed the Linearity Criterion, that no such errors were present. From this area of the curves, it was possible, using the established formula of Stefan-Boltzman* for radiation interchange, to compute the effective radiation area of our subjects. This analysis gave an effective radiation area of 74 to 75 per cent of the total DuBois surface area for our seated subjects. The specially designed experimental chair of canvas and metal used in these experiments did not alter the normal sitting posture. Hardy and DuBois,[49]

* $R' = K_R(T_W{}^4 - T_S{}^4)$; where K_R is the universal radiation constant (4.92 × 10^{-8} kg.-cal. per square meter per hour); T_W the equivalent wall temperature in degrees Absolute; and T_S the mean skin temperature in the same terms.

at the Russell Sage Institute of Pathology, found by two methods, an effective radiation area of 78 per cent for a man in a "mummy" position. These values correspond well with Bohnenkamp's figure of 85 per cent for a standing subject in a "spread eagle" position, since both the sitting and mummy postures obviously reduce effective radiation surface.

Using the figure of 75 per cent of the DuBois area for effective radiation area, the heat interchange component due to radiation could be measured in later experiments.

In a subsequent study, with low temperatures and increased air movement, we computed a radiation area which was 71 per cent, instead of 75 per cent of the DuBois area. We are inclined to attribute this to the tendency of the subjects to protect themselves against cold conditions by holding the legs close together and the arms close to the body.

Actual values for radiative heat interchange in our experiments ranged, for one subject, from a radiative heat loss of 39 calories per square meter per hour (with mean radiant temperature of the booth at 19°C) to a radiative heat gain of 89 calories per square meter per hour (with mean radiant temperature of the booth at 56.3°C); the corresponding figures for the second subject showed an extreme radiative loss of 44 calories (M.R.T., 19°C), and an extreme radiative gain of 91 calories (M.R.T., 59°C).

The sensitivity of the human skin to heat radiation is extraordinary. Oppel and Hardy[100] found that when the forehead was exposed to very delicately graded varying radiation, an increase in radiation intensity of 0.0014 calorie per square centimeter per second caused a rise in skin temperature of 0.003°C in three seconds, and this was sufficient to provoke a sensation of warmth. The face, as a whole, is very sensitive to heat, the backs of the hands somewhat less, and the upper arms much less sensitive.

Measurement of Heat Interchange Due to Convection

It is obvious that heat loss by convection includes a minor

component, the heat required to warm inspired air, and a major component, heat absorbed by the ambient air from the exterior surfaces of the body. It would be possible to estimate the first component from the temperatures of inspired and expired air and the volume of the air breathed in and out, but the procedure we have devised gives a measure of both combined.

Convective heat loss from the body surface depends on four basic factors. These are: the mean temperature of the external surfaces of the body (or of the clothing); area of surface exposed to convective heat loss; mean dry bulb temperature of the ambient air; and the rate of air movement. All four factors can be directly observed. The surface area, in this case, corresponds approximately to the DuBois area, although effectively it must be slightly less. The mean skin temperature was recorded, as described above, at fifteen points on the body surface.

Ambient air temperature was recorded in our earlier experiments by a recording potentiometer from three tiers of thermocouples at shoulder, mid-trunk, and knee levels. Air movement was recorded by a hot-wire anemometer held 6 inches from the body, over the fifteen points used for determining skin temperatures. In later studies, with higher air movements, we found it more accurate to determine air movement in the area to be occupied by the subject before his entrance into the booth.

After making these experimental observations, it was necessary to determine the quantitative influence of air movement upon the rate of convective heat loss so that the actual number of calories related to a given air temperature and air velocity could be computed.[138] This was done by conducting a series of 173 experiments in which air movement (at rates between 15 and 70 feet per minute) was the primary variable. Metabolism and evaporation were recorded, and radiation and heat change in the body computed by the procedures outlined above. The algebraic sum of metabolism, evaporation, radiation, and bodily heat change should represent heat interchange due to convection. This computed heat loss by convection was plotted against the difference between mean skin temperature and ambient air temperature, as indicated in Figure 4.

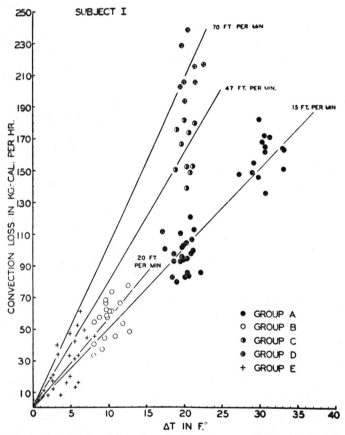

Figure 4. Relation of heat loss by convection to differences between skin and air temperature at varying air velocities. Group A, 15 feet per minute; Group B, 20 feet per minute; Group C, 47 feet per minute; Group D, 70 feet per minute; Group E, unrecorded.

There are two problems involved here: the form of the curve relating changes in air velocity to heat loss, and the actual constants involved, with the body in a certain posture.

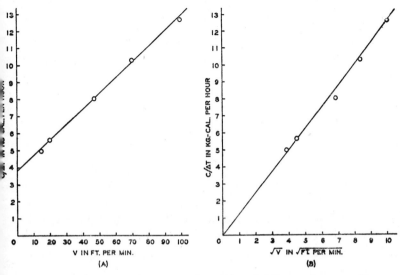

Figure 5. Relation between convection loss (C) and difference between skin temperature and air temperature (ΔT) plotted against air velocity and against the square root of air velocity.

In the first problem, physicists have employed two formulas. One involves a linear relationship in which different constants are assumed for "free convection" and for the additional cooling added by air movement. The second formula is a much simpler one, employing a single constant and assuming that heat loss varies with the square root of the air velocity.* A subsequent study, in which velocity was raised to 100 feet per minute, gave the results indicated in Figure 5. The left-hand graph represents the relation of convection loss per degree difference between skin and air plotted against air movement according to the two-term linear formula; the right-hand graph, the same data plotted against the one-term square-root formula.[37] Obviously the square-root formula makes no sense in the absence of any air movement; but this fact is of no

---

* $C = A\sqrt{V}\Delta T$; where C is convection loss; A is an experimentally determined constant; $\sqrt{V}$, the square root of air velocity, and ΔT, the difference between skin and air temperatures.

practical importance, since what we call "still air" always has a movement of 10 to 15 feet per minute. Whether the formula would hold for very high air movements, we do not know.

The values which we shall cite in connection with this convection formula we believe to be especially useful, since they were determined under conditions which, in ranges of air movement and in conditions of subject activity, are of special importance in ordinary life. Practical values which have been previously reported by other methods for the convection fraction vary greatly. However, this variation is an indication of the sensitivity of the convection loss to posture and to even slight movements of the subject, particularly at low air movements. Büttner[19] obtained a value for natural convection in "still air" of about 2.12 kg.-cal./m.^{2}/hr./°C, but his subject was motionless on a table with, perhaps, 30 to 40 per cent of his area in contact with table surface rather than air.

In a series of studies by Hardy and DuBois in the Russell Sage Calorimeter, the "still air" values for convection loss varied from .8 to 1.4 kg.-cal./m.^{2}/hr./°C, with subjects lying very quietly in a net hammock and with exceptionally low air movements; but with slight subject activity total convection loss rose to 4.0 to 5.8 kg.-cal./m^2/hr./°C, a level typical of the "still air" of the partitional calorimeter.

As to the range of velocities within which such formulas as ours can be expected to hold, it is probably wise to treat the indoor and outdoor range of velocities separately, and to consider that our present data are most useful in the range from still air to several hundred feet per minute, that is, 2 miles per hour and under. For the higher outdoor velocities, we know that near air movements of 80 miles per hour,[58] increases of velocity no longer increase cooling effects proportionately, since frictional forces interfere. For those interested in comparing the findings at indoor velocities with the higher outdoor ranges, the work of Plummer[104] may be consulted. In his report Plummer shows that for very wide velocity ranges the human body loses heat by convective processes in a manner similar to the convective heat loss of a cylinder 7 cm. in diameter.

To return to the conditions of the convection studies in the partitional calorimeter which were designed to analyze the most representative life situations, we may conclude that the square-root formula is efficient for reasonable velocities. It certainly would not correspond to strong blasts of air coming from one direction only. It seems certain, however, that for ordinary turbulent air flow of moderate intensities, either formula would be applicable. In our own studies we have, therefore, used the simpler single-term formula. This formula has been validated by Bedford and Warner in England for the Globe Thermometer. In our own experiments we have compared actual values of convection loss obtained by difference between metabolism, radiation, evaporation, and heat change in the body with convection loss computed from the square-root formula, and found a probable error of less than 4 per cent of the metabolic rate.[138]

Our next step was to determine the actual constant to be used in the equation. This constant A (see footnote, page 49) was found to be 0.65 $\times$ the DuBois area of the body (means for four different subjects ranging from 0.58 to 0.71).[37] It should, of course, be understood that this constant applies only to subjects seated in a chair as they were in our experiments. Aldrich found that a copper cylinder lost 40 per cent of its heat by convection in a vertical position, and 46 per cent in a horizontal position. The convective loss of a completely reclining subject should be greater, and the loss of a standing subject less than in a seated position, under exactly comparable conditions of air movement.

In our experiments we have recorded convection heat interchanges ranging from a gain of 2 calories per square meter (with an air temperature of 35.4°C and an air velocity of 15 to 20 feet per minute) to a loss of 100 calories per square meter (with an air temperature of 21.4°C and an air velocity of 70 feet per minute).

Combined Influence of Various Environmental Factors

Numerous attempts have been made in the past to simplify the measurement of the various environmental factors influencing human comfort. In England, the Dufton Eupatheoscope[28] and the Vernon Globe Thermometer,[124] and in this country an instrument called the Thermo-Integrator[132] were devised in the hope of recording a single figure which would indicate the combined influence of air temperature, air movement, relative humidity, and mean radiant temperature upon human comfort. All these attempts have been abandoned as the various investigators discovered that the physiological reactions of the human body (to be discussed in Chapter III) vary so widely at different points in the temperature scale that no single physical instrument can provide a true picture of the environmental influences concerned. Only an independent determination of the four distinct factors mentioned above can give a real measure of the thermal demands of the environment.[64]

The Research Laboratory of the American Society of Heating and Ventilating Engineers at Pittsburgh approached the subject from another standpoint. Its investigators measured the temperature, velocity, and relative humidity of the air (ignoring radiation effects, since air and walls were at the same temperature). They then obtained from their subjects votes as to the relative comfort of the conditions maintained, and prepared a graph of "effective temperatures" representing (at several rates of air velocity) the combination of air temperature and relative humidity yielding equal sensations of comfort. These graphs have become standard for practice in air conditioning, and have given reasonably satisfactory results under hot conditions. There is serious question, however, as to their validity under environmental conditions which are in the cool to moderate range, and recent modifications have been suggested[112] which should remedy the previous undue allowance for the warming effect of high humidities in the moderate comfort range.

In our own studies we felt that a figure representing the combined influence of air temperature and mean radiant temperature might be of value since the physiological reactions to these two factors are so similar (as is not the case where evaporative response to relative humidity is in question). We therefore derived a factor which we have called "operative temperature," [139] defined as the sum of the radiation constant multiplied by the mean wall temperature, and the convection constant multiplied by the mean air temperature, divided by the sum of the two constants.* The operative temperature is not a physical condition, since it is weighted by the factors of convection area, radiation area, and air movement; but it is a measure of heat demand which allows for the physiological reactions involved. When air movement is moderate (30 to 35 feet per minute), however, the convection and radiation constants are very close to each other, and operative temperature is not far from the mean of air and mean radiant temperatures. For the conditions which obtain in ordinary indoor spaces, the engineer can safely assume a mean between air and wall temperatures as representing operative temperature.

Analyses of skin temperatures and bodily heat change at operative temperatures, obtained under experimental conditions with widely different convective and radiative components, have revealed an interesting phenomenon.[56] We have found that under cold conditions (operative temperature below 31°C for the nude subject), the skin temperature is lower (and the chilling of body tissues greater) at a given operative temperature with cool air and warm walls than

---

* $T_O = \dfrac{K_R T_W + K_C T_A}{K_R + K_C}$

where $K_R = A_R (4 k_R T_S{}^3)$,

and $K_C = k_c \sqrt{V}$.

under the reverse conditions. That is, the cool air component exerts a slightly greater effect than would have been predicted. With hot walls and cold air, the skin temperature is 1 to 1.5°C lower than with the same operative temperature maintained by air and walls of identical temperature. This differential effect is probably not due to any specific differences in the effect of convection and radiation upon the skin, but to the fact that heat losses from the respiratory tract and those due to increased heat loss caused by slight body movements are governed only by air temperature.

Heat Changes in the Temperature of Body Tissues

When the body is in balance with its thermal environment, the algebraic sum of metabolism minus evaporative heat loss plus-or-minus convective heat interchange plus-or-minus radiative heat interchange is equal to zero. When the balance is not perfect, as in the transitional periods studied in our experiments, this is not the case, and for a time skin temperatures and the general temperature of the body tissues may rise or fall.

In our earlier studies we denoted such change in body temperature by the term "storage" and defined this factor in such a way that chilling of body tissues was represented by positive "storage" and heating of the body by negative "storage." This convention was convenient for the mathematical computations which we desired to make. It tends to be confusing, however, because it involves the conception that a positive figure represents a chilling of the body, or what amounts to a "storage" of coldness. We shall use, in the present discussion, a more psychologically acceptable term, "Heat Change of the Body," or "Heat Change" for short, a figure identical with "storage" but of opposite sign. What we now call "Heat Change" (ΔH) is the same component discussed in our earlier papers as "storage" but with a plus value for heating of the body and a negative value for cooling of the body.* The figure, as in the case of all other components, refers to an hourly rate of change.

Under warm and hot environmental conditions a rise in rectal temperature appears to yield a reasonably close measure of Heat Change. This is illustrated by the linearity of the curve plotted in Figure 5, up to the point where evaporation of sweat ceases to keep pace with its secretion.

In cold atmospheres, on the other hand, changes in rectal temperature cease to be indicative of Heat Change, since the exterior of the body cools much more rapidly than the interior. Hardy and DuBois computed the actual temperature of the body (in the air temperature range between 23° and 35°C for nude subjects) by multiplying rectal temperature by 4 and skin temperature by 1, and dividing the sum by 5. Burton (at an environmental temperature of 23°C with lightly clothed subjects) multiplied rectal temperature by approximately 2 and skin temperature by 1, and divided by 3. The DuBois ratio of 4 to 1 assumes that the skin temperature represents a layer of tissue extending 1 centimeter below the surface. It is interesting and surprising to note that a surface layer 1 cm. deep includes 21 per cent of the weight of a 70-kilogram man, and a layer 2.5 cm. deep includes about one-half that weight.

Our own studies[133] have led us to the conclusion that the DuBois formula corresponds reasonably well to the warm conditions maintained in our experiments, while the Burton formula more nearly corresponds to cold conditions.

* For an equation expressing an algebraic sum = 0 of certain classes of heat exchange, situations are conceivable (refrigerated mannikins) in which any element might be plus or minus, including heat production (M is negative for refrigeration) and evaporation (E is positive for condensation). When the equation is used in a physiological framework, M is always plus, E is always minus, and R and C, plus or minus, depending upon the value of air and surface temperatures relative to skin temperature.

In this book M, E, C, R, and ΔH are obviously defined as scalar quantities, their directions being given by the signs attached to them in equations.

One of the major advantages of partitional calorimetry is, however, that we need not depend on arbitrary assumptions of the relative weight to be given to skin temperature and rectal temperature. After determining the constants governing convection and radiation, Heat Change can be directly computed by difference. By this procedure we have obtained values of Heat Change ranging from $+10$ calories per square meter (with air at $35.4°C$ and walls at $36.6°C$) to -58 calories per square meter (with air at $17.1°C$ and walls at $19°C$).

From a large series of experiments[144] we have prepared the averages indicated in the tables below. Table I shows mean

TABLE I

Series	Air temp.	No. expt.	Body temperature computed on ratio of rectal temperature to skin temperature of				Decrease in body temperature from Series A on ratio of			
			1:1	2:1	3:1	4:1	1:1	2:1	3:1	4:1
A	35°+	30	36.4	36.7	36.9	37.0				
B	30–34°	48	36.3	36.6	36.8	36.9	.1	.1	.1	.1
C	25–29°	30	35.0	35.7	36.1	36.2	1.4	1.0	.8	.8
D	20–24°	18	34.6	35.4	35.7	36.0	1.8	1.3	1.2	1.0
E	Under 20°	6	33.2	34.4	34.9	35.3	3.2	2.3	2.0	1.7

TABLE II

Series	Heat Change[1] computed as ratio of				Observed Heat Change
	1:1	2:1	3:1	4:1	
B	7	7	7	7	12
C	92	66	53	53	51
D	119	86	79	66	110
E	211	152	132	112	164

[1] Temperature difference multiplied by weight of subject (79 kg.) × .83.

temperatures for the body as a whole, computed from rectal temperature and mean skin temperature in four different ways, using ratios of rectal temperature to body temperature of 1:1, 1:2, 1:3, and 1:4, respectively. The experiments are averaged in five groups of air temperature, from hot (over 35°C) to cold (under 20°C). The last half of Table I shows the difference in body temperature as thus determined between the hot atmosphere and each successive lower air temperature. In Table II we have computed the heat change in the body for each of Conditions B, C, D, and E (as compared with Condition A), by multiplying the difference in body temperature by the weight of the subject (79 kg.) and by .83 (the specific heat of the body).

It will be noted that for Conditions B and C the actually observed heat change (last column) corresponds closely with the DuBois ratio of 4:1 for weighting rectal and skin temperatures. For the cold conditions (under 24°C for the nude subject) the observed values indicate a ratio even lower than that of Burton, somewhere between 2:1 and 1:1. This is entirely reasonable since, in transitional states, such as those we have studied, the area of superficial chilling of tissues may well extend for several centimeters below the surface. For normal equilibrium conditions, the DuBois formula seems justified. For temporary exposure to cold, we must go even below the Burton ratio.

General Physical Phenomena of Heat Interchange

The thermal interchanges between the body and its environment are fully expressed by the formula:

$$M - E \pm C \pm R = \triangle H, \text{ or}$$

$$M - E \pm A_R K (\triangle T_W) \pm A_C (\triangle T_A) \sqrt{V} = \triangle H.$$

All units are expressed in kilogram-calories per hour.

M = observed rate of metabolism,

53

E = rate of cooling due to the sweat actually evaporated,

C = rate of cooling due to convection,

A_R = the effective radiation area for a given subject in a given position, in square meters,

K = $(4k\ T_s^3)$ from the first approximation of Stefan's law, k, being the universal radiation constant,

ΔT_W = difference between skin temperature and mean radiant temperature in °C,

A_C = the convection constant for a given subject in a given position,

ΔT_A = the difference between skin temperature and air temperature in °C,

V = mean turbulent velocity of air movement in cm/sec.,

ΔH = change in mean body temperature.

The actual relative magnitude of the heat interchange by various avenues may vary within wide limits. It is sometimes stated that radiation accounts for about two-fifths of the heat loss from the body, convection for two-fifths, and evaporation for one-fifth. This is approximately true for a resting subject at moderate environmental temperature with little air movement, low relative humidity, and air and walls of about the same temperature. The mean of six of our experiments with a nude subject with both air and walls at 24.3°C, showed that 21 per cent of the actual heat lost to the environment was due to evaporation, 37 per cent to radiation, and 42 per cent to convection.

Variations in atmospheric conditions will, however, produce the most diverse ratios. DuBois[26] cites the figures at the top of page 55.

Our own experiments are shown at the bottom of page 55.

In Experiment A, the body temperature was falling, show-

Conditions	Temp. °C	Calories per hour, Pro- duced	Calories per hour, Esti- mated	Per cent heat loss Rad.	Per cent heat loss Conv.	Per cent heat loss Evap.
Basal, pajamas & sheet	25.0	68.1	76.6	53	19	28
Basal, nude	25.0	64.1	85.0	67	10	23
Exercise, nude	25.0	125.3	105.3	53	25	22
Basal, nude with fan	29.4	68.5	80.4	41	33	26
Basal, nude	34.7	67.3	72.8	5	7	88
Basal, nude with fan	34.7	69.5	79.1	4	6	90

ing a rate of chilling of the body-tissues 42 per cent above the rate of metabolic heat production.

In Experiment B the body was gaining more heat by radiation than it was producing in metabolism.

In Experiment C the convection loss was greatly increased by high air movement (264 cm. per second).

In Experiment D the body was gaining heat by radiation at a rate 66 per cent above the metabolic rate.

In Experiment E the body was gaining heat from both air

			Percentage of actual heat loss to the environment by various avenues		
Series	Air temp. °C	Wall temp. °C	Heat loss due to Evaporation	Heat loss due to Radiation	Heat loss due to Convection
A	17.1	19.0	10	40	50
B	16.0	49.1	21		79
C	22.8	22.8	17	13	70
D	29.4	52.4	78		22
E	35.4	36.6	100		

and walls, and evaporation was the only avenue of heat loss.

Clearly, no statement as to the percentage relation of various avenues of heat loss can have general validity. The methods of partitional calorimetry, however, make it relatively easy to predict what will happen under a given set of circumstances.

There is much more to be done with this technique, however, before the picture of environmental effects upon heat loss from the body is in any sense complete. In particular, the complex subject of unilateral influences of radiation effects and of air movement impinging on one side of the body has not been touched; and the constants for high rates of turbulent air flow and of non-turbulent air flow should be determined.

It is clear, however, that heat interchanges basically depend upon the definite physical and physiological factors tabulated below.

	Evaporation	Convection	Radiation
Physical factors:			
Air temperature	+	+	
Air movement	+	+	
Relative humidity	+		
Mean radiant temp.			+
Physiological factors:			
DuBois surface area		+	
Effective rad. area			+
Area of evaporating surface	+		
Mean skin temp.		+	+
Available moisture for evaporation	+		

Of the five physiological factors involved, the DuBois surface area and the effective radiation area are experimental constants, which can be determined for a given subject in a given position by the methods outlined above. The physiological reactions governing skin temperature and those governing area of evaporating surface and available moisture for evaporation (which may be expressed by a single factor) will be discussed in Chapter III; and the practical procedures of air conditioning by which we can control the four[64] physical environmental factors involved, will be discussed in Chapters V and VI.

CHAPTER III

THE ADAPTATIONS OF THE HUMAN BODY TO VARYING THERMAL CONDITIONS

Characteristics and Significance of Human Temperature Regulation

ONE of the major achievements of biological evolution is the acquisition by birds and mammals of the power of maintaining a constant body temperature, somewhere between 35° and 40°C. The lower forms of life which assume or approach the temperature of the environment are the slaves of this environment, so that at low temperatures they can only hibernate in a state of suspended animation. To maintain constant body temperature, a complex mechanism is needed to govern heat production or heat loss, or both, so as to maintain a high and even level of tissue activity under varying external conditions.

The importance of a regulated body temperature, as a necessary condition of intelligent, sensitive human life as we know it, can scarcely be overestimated. Students of any special field relating to one of the many organs or functions of the human body can demonstrate the awkward deficiencies to which life would be subject if the particular piece of biological apparatus which intrigues them were not so uniquely developed to implement the functions of the whole body system. And this is natural, since the thing we regard as the whole is necessarily incomplete if any of its parts or functions are absent. Nonetheless, we may, with justice, maintain that the evolution of an exactly regulated deep body temperature set the stage for the

58

development of the behavior capacities fundamental to learning, thinking, and acting in the continuous, cumulative, and stable fashion which we regard as the essence of free and intelligent life.

To survey this evolutionary story would require much labor. We may, however, outline certain significant features with profit to our appreciation of the more immediate interests of this book. Surely, in the evolution of warm-blooded animal types, a very important item has been the development of animal tissues whose chemical systems endow them with high combustion rates; in short, tissues whose rate of heat production per gram of tissue is such that the active tissue is necessarily substantially above the external environment in temperature. In cold-blooded animals, whose heat production and tissue temperature follow the temperature of the outer world, tissue temperatures are generally above those in the environment, but the net difference is small. Hence we may regard the biological invention of tissues with potentially high rates of combustion as an important precursor of the thermally regulated man.

The mutational combination of such instances of metabolic power with experiments in variation of body size and insulative covering must eventually have resulted in heat-producing organisms fulfilling by accident or design certain optimal relations between heat-producing capacity per unit of weight, absolute size, and insulative covering. The optimal relations are complex, but a simple example may give us a sense of the problem. An electric heater of 300 watt capacity is placed in a metal shed the size of an ordinary room. Let the resistance wires of the heater be very long and of such diameter that their total heating effect is produced by wire temperatures only 2° to 3°C above room temperature. This is a clumsy arrangement but reasonably comparable, in a thermal sense, to the type of tissue with low metabolic power. If we now allow the outside air to vary from 0° to 30°C, we will note that our metal-shed temperature has insufficient heat to compensate for this change, and generally will have a temperature only a degree or two above the outer air. If our heater wire is of such material that its resistance changes with temperature, we may also note that the heat input is greatly reduced from 300 to perhaps 100 watts when the outer temperature reaches 0°. This is, in bare outline, thermal behavior analogous to that of the cold-blooded animal types in an environment of variable temperature.

In order to make this primitive ineffective heating arrangement satisfactory, we may do several things. By insulating the walls very heavily we may make the same amount of heat produce a larger temperature difference. This is comparable to the evolution of a thicker skin, fur, feathers, or, in a certain sense, to the development of a larger absolute size without change of intensity of heat production per unit weight (smaller exposed surface in relation to total heat-producing mass). Or, substituting materials whose resistance is not greatly influenced by temperature, we may make the system deliver its full 300 watts at 0° as well as at 30°C temperature. This effect is comparable to the development of tissue oxidative systems with relatively low temperature coefficients. We might also increase the heat input to 3000 watts, or reduce the size of the shed (an effect comparable to development of higher rates of combustion per unit of tissue weight); in any case we would greatly increase the average temperature difference between the inner structure and the outer regions. These procedures or combinations of them would give us a potentially large difference in temperature and remove the decline of heat production with lower outside temperatures. We might now decide to select some temperature such as 37°C as a desirable inside shed temperature. This temperature may be maintained, provided we introduce the equivalent of a thermostat, a device to turn on heat whenever the temperature falls below 37°. Or we may adjust the heat input to remain constant, at a value sufficient to produce 37° inside at 0° outside, but mechanically introduce outer air to hold this inner temperature as outer temperature rises toward 30°C.

Although these analogies are crude, the warm-blooded animals, by natural variation and selection, have evolved similar temperature-regulating devices which by variation of effective insulation, outer skin circulation of blood, and level of heat production are successful in maintaining a deep body temperature which varies only 1° to 2°C, despite environmental variations of 30° to 40°C, and variations in heat output which may be ten-fold under conditions of strenuous activity. The balance of heat production and heat loss thus obtained in association with a nearly constant deep body temperature is truly remarkable. The average individual produces about 2500 kg.-cal. of heat each day, an amount of heat sufficient to raise 25 liters of water from freezing to boiling. The actual heat production varies from a basal level during sleep or rest to a value two to three times above basal with moderate work, and the environmental temperature varies seasonally by as much as 40°C. Despite these variations, an oral temperature at rest is usually 37°C ±0.5°, and even with strenuous exercise this level does not increase by more than 1° to 2°. Some elevation of body temperature above the normal level may occur as a regulated effect in exercise, higher tissue temperatures being apparently advantageous during muscular work.[97]

In emphasizing the preciseness of deep-tissue temperature control in the human body, it is very necessary to realize that the temperature of the body as a whole is not so precisely controlled. This concept is of particular interest in the present discussion, since the variation which occurs in the temperature of the outer skin, subcutaneous fat, and muscle tissue as central temperature is held constant is a most important item in determining human comfort under various environmental heat, cold, and humidity stresses. Bazett[7] has given a very clear discussion of this interdependence of a constant internal temperature and a variable peripheral tissue temperature. He points out that the temperature that is controlled is not the temperature of the body as a whole, nor its average temperature, but primarily the temperature of the deep central areas such as the heart, lungs, abdominal organs and brain. Under resting conditions, the concentration of heat production is also in these deeply situated central structures, and this fact alone greatly facilitates good temperature control. The location of heat production in exercise, however, is primarily in the peripheral muscles, and the fact that our heat regulation also operates efficiently under these circumstances is further proof of the remarkable character of the regulative apparatus. Bazett has estimated that under resting conditions the following percentages of the total metabolic heat are generated in the indicated locations: peripheral muscles, 20 per cent; respiratory and circulatory apparatus, 10 per cent; brain, 20 per cent; with about 50 per cent attributed to the glandular activities of the liver, intestines, and kidneys. Hence, about 80 per cent of the total resting heat has a central origin. In moderate exercise the total heat production may rise to 3 or 4 times the resting level. Under these circumstances, however, 75 to 80 per cent of the total heat is generated in the peripheral muscles. We see, therefore, that our heat regulation devices are not only adapted to regulate a single pattern of relative heat production, but are quite equal to the task of dealing with very large changes in the ratio of central and peripheral heat production.

Before proceeding with the description of experimental means of determining the way in which the human body achieves a balance of heat production and heat loss under various exposures, we may briefly sketch the primary characteristics of the control system which is basic to human temperature regulation. There are many interesting analogies between these processes and temperature control devices with which we are familiar in every day life, and mention of these similarities will make it easier for the reader to understand the discussions which follow.

In order to maintain internal temperature within a narrow range, around 37°C, the body has at its disposal a first line defense in the heat capacity effects of the extremities and peripheral skin and tissue. When the individual is thermally comfortable, the skin of the toes may be at 27°, that of the upper legs and arms at 31° to 32°, with forehead temperatures near 34° to 35°, and deep body temperatures at 37° to 38°C. Between those surfaces substantially below 37°C and the deep central region of relatively constant temperature lies a skin and tissue mass of variable temperature. When the individual moves from a comfortable atmosphere to one uncomfortably cool, the cooler peripheral regions are allowed to fall still further in temperature. In addition, average blood flow through these regions is greatly reduced by constriction of small peripheral blood vessels. With reduced blood flow the full insulation value of peripheral skin and fat is realized, and the temperature in deeper body zones is protected. On exposure to moderate heat, the process is reversed. Extensive networks of blood vessels just beneath the skin dilate maximally and as much as 50 to 60 per cent of the total blood pumped by the heart may be circulated through this peripheral cooling system. In principle the action is very similar to the thermostatic regulator which maintains automobile engines at a proper temperature by restricting the flow to the radiator on a cold morning and increasing it later as engine temperatures become optimal. Associated with the blood vessel effects, which by regulation of peripheral circulation utilize capacity effects and tissue insulation changes, are more complex reactions affecting general behavior. Thus, the cold-stressed individual may be motivated to increase clothing, to increase heat production through exercise, or to leave the uncomfortable environment. Similarly appropriate reactions are stimulated under heat stress. Heat regulation of the type described is typical of the reaction to moderate heat and cold, and its principal feature is vasomotor control of peripheral insulation through circulatory changes. A very large part of what we feel as unsatisfactory or uncomfortable in usual thermal experience is closely associated with this active vasomotor heat regulation. We apparently all prefer a thermal environment in which our skin sensations are inconspicuous, and in which our peripheral circulation is not particularly burdened with the task of maintaining a continuous vasoconstriction or dilation in peripheral areas.

Against greater extremes of cold or heat, the body possesses adaptation possibilities which are much more efficient for heat stress than for cold stress. When subject to extreme cold, we may prolong our period of survival by peripheral vasoconstriction, but ultimately significant protection is primarily a matter of clothing. Plunging the body into a bath at 4° may increase bodily heat production ten-fold through the intense shivering which follows continued cooling persisting after maximum peripheral blood vessel constriction. But this is extremely expensive in energy-accounting; body reserves are soon exhausted, and significant protection against extreme cold is essentially a matter of adequate clothing, high food intakes playing a detectable but not impressive role through maintenance of higher heat production.

On exposure to severe heat, however, the body brings into play a new and powerful defense against increases of deep temperature above 37°–38°. On moving from a comfortable to a hot environment, the initially cool peripheral regions of the body are perfused by warm blood flowing through a widely dilated peripheral network. If the heat stress is great, the thermal capacity effect represented by the initially cool periphery is soon exhausted and skin temperatures over the whole body approach 35°C. At or near this point, despite increasing external heat stress, they tend to become stabilized. This occurs as a result of strong stimulation of sweat glands which pour out onto the body surfaces large quantities of fluid for evaporation. As long as the physical conditions of the surrounding air will evaporate moisture from the skin, the body's heat regulation system continues to secrete these quantities of fluid, which, through evaporation, may maintain a relatively cool skin (35° to 36°) and a stable deep temperature (37° to

38°), despite air temperatures which at low humidities may be greatly in excess of body temperature.

These highly organized thermal defenses—vasomotor regulation, shivering, sweat secretion, and correlated adaptive behavior of higher order—are the result of cooperative action of two primary regions of temperature sensitivity, the skin surface with its temperature receptors, and a dual nervous control center or correlator located in the brain (hypothalamus). This center is stimulated by sensory impulses from the hot and cold receptors located mainly in the skin, and by the temperature of the blood perfusing the center itself. This center is said to be dual in nature, since by surgical operation on animals it is possible to show that most of the heat conserving reactions (constriction, shivering, etc.) are concentrated in one region, while those concerned with heat dissipation are nearby but likewise distinctly grouped. After appropriate hypothalamic operations[106] animals may retain their normal ability to shiver, vasoconstrict, and in other ways to combat cold, but when subject to heat stress will be unable to bring the heat-dissipating mechanisms into action.

Such a brief introductory sketch of a very complicated subject, as a preparation for our consideration of human reactions in experiments which bear on normal adjustment of heat production and heat loss, can serve two purposes. It provides a general picture of the manner in which body heat capacity and heat production, variable peripheral circulation, and evaporative reactions are called upon by a sensitive internal control center, utilizing both a surface and a deep body temperature sensitive apparatus, to achieve a very efficient regulation of the temperature of the central body region containing our most vital organic systems. In the second instance, and as a return to our initial emphasis on the importance of this central stability of temperature for intelligent life, it serves as a background for an illustration of man's behavior under temperature stress which we feel throws considerable light on the average person's subjective reactions to moderate but long continued exposure to inequable thermal conditions.

To gain this overall subjective sense of the personal factors which are subtly affected when thermal conditions are not ideal, let us look at the extremes of human postural reaction to thermal stress. Imagine a nude subject placed in a cooled chamber at sub-zero temperatures. After a sufficient length of time, he will be found in a rigid posture, arms and legs folded against the body and fixed in a general pattern of contracted muscular rigidity. Although this posture may have been preceded by stimulation with violent exercise and bouts of shivering, observation[36] would confirm the fact that from the very beginning the subject has reacted to the cold with a basic pattern in which sharp increase in muscle tension is the most conspicuous factor. In due time voluntary inhibition of this pattern of muscle contraction becomes impossible and the individual is locked in a tightly contracted posture so severe that even the respiratory muscles are affected and breathing becomes extremely difficult. This rigidity is not due in any sense to being frozen stiff. If the exposure persists, at death his musculature will temporarily relax. Such a subject in reality is exhibiting the ultimate degree of a deep-seated actively organized and involuntary reflex to cold which is a basic part of temperature regulation. Such contracted postures reduce the surface area for heat loss, and in earlier stages provide a strong stimulus for both exercise and involuntary shivering, as means of increasing heat production.

Contrast this picture with that of the man exposed to a temperature of 60° to 70°C. We see no initial period of active stimulation, no sharply defined postures indicating high muscle tone. Instead of standing or running, the subject droops in a listless fashion. Posture, in the ordinary sense of the word, decays, and upright stance requires voluntary effort. In due time, after exhaustive sweating and body dehydration, the subject sinks to the floor. Here he lies in a relaxed spread-eagle attitude, muscles limp and his body exposing maximum surface to the environment. In contrast to the labored respiration and slow pulse of the cold exposure, the heat victim has a rapid shallow respiration and elevated pulse rate. Aside from such physiological details, we are principally impressed by the picture presented of extreme muscular relaxation and the absence of a positive organized posture.

Such extremes of heat or cold exposure are seldom either seen or experienced by the average person. In both cases we note that temperature regulation has been unequal to stress and that immobility, and perhaps death, follow the deviation of the deep body temperature from its tolerable range in either direction. The intimate physiology of the respiratory, circulatory, and body fluid chemical changes that occur at either extreme, are beyond our interests here. However, the dramatic and sharply contrasting postural and muscular effects of the two extreme thermal situations may be readily appreciated, and the probable subjective character of the two different types of stress easily imagined.

What is important for the appreciation of the nature of ordinary ranges of thermal discomfort is the fact that the above illustrations dramatize the extremes of a continuous body function, namely, dynamic maintenance of posture and the alternating postures which comprise physical activity in relation to temperature and the conditions of body heat production and loss. Our subjective sense of the activity and adequacy of the postural functions is difficult to describe, but it is certain that this subjective element is one of the highly important components of our personal sense of comfort and well-being. There are many reservations and qualifications necessary for a full scientific description of the effect of thermal influences on efficiency and subjective comfort. Basically, however, we may say with assurance that the progressive decay of posture in warm environments, and its accentuation, breaking over into a desire for physical action in cool environments, are extreme examples of a marked reflex association between temperature and posture regulation mechanisms. At the extremes of exposure we are not able, by voluntary effort, to support a posture contrary to the pattern set by this association. We are completely immobile, rigid or relaxed according to the thermal circumstances. In the usual range of environmental temperatures we may choose to work quietly despite a vague but persistent urge for movement, or we may work resolutely at a task despite a recurrent desire to relax and take it easy. Postural accentuation or inhibition incongruent with the activity at hand may, no doubt, arise from many sources, some of them of a social or psychological nature. One scientific end of physiologically acceptable air conditioning is, however, the production of thermal environments in which the involuntary component of posture maintenance is consonant with the requirements of particular types of work, rather than contrary to these requirements. Even though the deviation from an ideal atmosphere is slight, if the tasks in hand, or the pursuit of the interests and activities desired, do not permit an adjustment of activity or posture consonant with the subtle change of postural tone which is thermally determined, the individual experiences distraction and a subjective sense of effort which is unpleasant and fatiguing.

Our use of the term "posture" in these illustrations has been broad, in the lay sense of the term. Such use is, however, physiologically sound, and includes not only static postures, but the succession of postures which constitute organized movement. Such use also implies that the static posture is in reality a highly organized dynamic process representing not inaction but a well-integrated physiological activity. The reflex associations determining these postural reactions to temperature are primitive and deeply rooted in the nervous system of all warm-blooded organisms. Within moderate temperature ranges man, by consciously determined effort, may standardize his posture and activity, counter to persistent natural tendencies determined by his immediate thermal situation. No doubt the perennial interest in the weather as a topic of conversation, and the persistence with which the elusive concept of the ideal atmosphere has been investigated, both reflect a rational interest in an important problem, but also unconscious human acknowledgment of the fact that temperature regulation holds a top priority among involuntary neural functions, and one not always respected in our choice of working and living environments.

From these remarks it must be evident that the conditions determining heat exchange with man's environment are not only of great interest to biology, but that an understanding of this problem is fundamental to the scientific provision of atmospheric conditions conducive to health and comfort. In the remainder of this chapter a description of the technical approach to the problem of measuring the thermal effects sketched above will be given.

Changes in Heat Exchange with Varying Environmental Temperatures

The fundamental phenomena involved in this adaptive process in the case of man are illustrated by such a graph as that presented in Figure 6. The particular studies concerned included 35 different series of experiments with a single nude subject, observed in the usual semi-reclining posture. The abscissa represents operative temperatures, and the ordinate represents heat gain above the zero line and heat loss below the zero line in kilogram-calories per man per hour; and each circle of a given type corresponds to an independent group of experiments.

The upper line of the graph (crossed circles) indicates observed metabolism which in this case (a very stout subject weighing 230 pounds) showed a very slight tendency to increase with rising environmental temperatures. A minimum figure of 87 calories was observed at operative temperature of 18.5°, and a maximum value of 106 calories at a temperature of 28.5°, both exceptional. All other values were between 91 and 104 calories.

The open circles represent the heat interchange by convec-

SUBJECT I

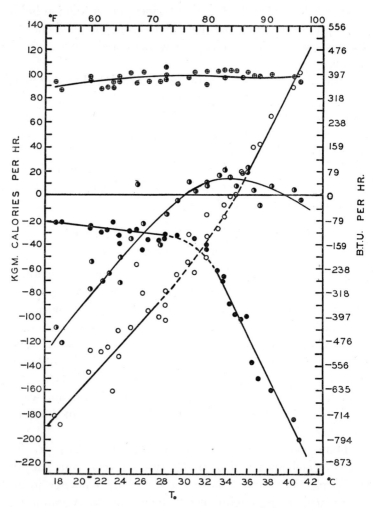

Figure 6. Factors in heat balance between the unclothed human body and its environment at various Operative Temperatures.

tion and radiation combined, since the abscissa is plotted on a basis of the operative temperature governing both processes. It will be noted that heat gain due to these factors (above an operative temperature of 35°) shows a straight line relationship to operative temperature. Below 35°, however, heat loss due to conduction plus radiation does not fall off as rapidly as operative temperature. The change in slope is due to physiological adaptation in the form of a decrease in skin temperature, which will be discussed in a succeeding paragraph.

The curve for evaporative heat loss (solid circles) shows a gradual increase in the cold zone, from 22 calories at 18.5° and 23.5° to 33 calories at 29.5°. Above 33°, evaporative heat loss increases very rapidly—to 61 at 33.5° and to 192 at 41°. The slight increase in evaporative cooling between 18° and 30° is due to the physical factor of changes in atmospheric vapor tension which produces greater evaporation at higher air temperatures. The rapid increase in evaporation above 30° is due to increased sweat secretion, which will be analyzed in a subsequent paragraph.

Heat Change is positive (the mean temperature of body tissues is rising) at operative temperatures above 30°, except in one single instance (with very high wall temperature), where a negative change of 9 calories was recorded. The positive values varied from 4 to 22 calories, and the fact that the higher figures appear between 30° and 36° (with low figures above 36°) may be coincidental or may be due to the very effective evaporative cooling at high temperatures. Except in one single instance, at operative temperatures below 30°, values for heat change were negative (cooling of body tissues). With minor deviations, the increase in negative heat change is steady from 6 calories at 29.5° to 123 calories and 110 calories at 18.5°.

Considering the graph as a whole, we note three major zones.

At operative temperatures between 29° and 33° (with the particular nude subject in semi-reclining position) there is a zone of essential thermal equilibrium. The mean of 36 indi-

71

vidual experiments in this zone shows a metabolism of 95 calories, a heat loss by conduction and convection combined of 47 calories, a heat loss by evaporation of 42 calories, and a positive Heat Change of 7 calories. This state of relative equilibrium is, therefore, characterized by a rather high ratio of evaporative cooling (47 per cent of total heat loss), indicating a substantial acceleration of sweat secretion above minimal values. The area of thermal equilibrium would, of course, be shifted up or down the operative temperature scale for a subject of different body build or in different positions, or for a clothed subject, or one performing physical work.

The mean values for a group of subjects[38] indicate thermal equilibrium between 29° and 33°, marked negative heat change appearing below 29°, and increased sweat secretion above 33°. With clothed subjects, on the other hand, the area of equilibrium (as might be expected) is wider and it occurs at a lower environmental temperature. Negative heat change began in this case only below 25° and active sweat secretion only above 29°. It is interesting to note that with a subject performing active physical work,[131] highly variable results were obtained. The highest positive figure was 83 calories (with no other positive value over 31); the highest negative value was —47 calories, although operative temperatures went as low as 12.4°. These are all heat changes per man (not per square meter), and the activity of the working subject corresponded to metabolic rates of over 300 calories. Figures for evaporative heat loss were also highly variable with active work, but they indicated onset of active sweat secretion at 19° to 21° operative temperature. The mean evaporative heat loss for two subjects at temperatures below 19° was 48 and above 21° was 152 calories.

Thus the area of thermal equilibrium may vary from 29° to 33° for the nude subject at rest to 19° to 21° for the same subject performing active work.

At operative temperatures below that of thermal equilibrium there is an area which we have called the "zone of body cooling." As one proceeds downward to successively lower environmental temperatures, heat loss due to radiation plus convection increases progressively, from 46 calories up to maxima (in our series of experiments) of 181 and 188 calories. In the same range, heat loss due to evaporation decreases only from 42 to 22 calories. The balance is taken up by Heat Change in the body tissues, which rises from −6 calories at equilibrium to −116 calories at operative temperatures of 18° and 18.5°. The slope of the line representing negative Heat Change is essentially parallel to the line representing heat loss by convection plus radiation.

Above operative temperatures of 33° (for the nude resting subject) lies what we have called the "zone of evaporative regulation." Here, as one passes to higher and higher environmental temperatures, heat loss due to convection plus radiation decreases, and above an operative temperature of 34° changes to a progressively increasing heat gain. While 46 calories were lost by this avenue at equilibrium, 102 calories were gained from the environment at an operative temperature of 41°. Increased heat loss from evaporation, however, balances this situation with remarkable precision, rising from 42 calories at equilibrium to 192 calories at 41° operative temperature. As a result of this adaptive process, there is no appreciable increase in positive Heat Change. The value of this factor was 6 calories for equilibrium and 4 calories for environments at 40° and over.

In general the results of the Pierce Laboratory experiments correspond with reasonable closeness to the findings of the earlier workers of the Laboratory of the American Society of Heating and Ventilating Engineers at Pittsburgh. The *Heating, Ventilating, and Air-Conditioning Guide* of the American Society of Heating and Ventilating Engineers[2] compares the two sets of data in a graph which shows general concordance, with the following exceptions. The metabolism in the A.S.-H.V.E. experiments was somewhat higher, as would be expected, since the subjects were not in a semi-reclining position in the Pittsburgh studies. The Pierce data show a greater heat loss by convection and radiation at low temperatures, and a higher heat gain by this avenue at high environmental temperatures, no doubt as a result of lighter clothing and the semi-reclining position. The most important difference between the graphs is in evaporative heat loss which, between air temperatures of 23° and 37°, was considerably higher in the Pittsburgh experiments than in those conducted at New Haven. The reason for this deviation is not wholly clear. At 29°, for example, the metabolism of the Pittsburgh subjects was about 54, and the evaporative heat loss about 33 calories per square meter, while at New Haven, data showed a metabolism of 47 and an evaporative heat loss of 16 calories, while the heat loss due to radiation and convection was about 24 in both cases. This difference occurs close to the point where evaporative thermal adjustment begins. At 31° the New Haven subjects showed an evaporative rate of 27 instead of 16 calories. Apparently evaporative regulation began at a somewhat lower temperature in the subjects used at Pittsburgh, and in the absence of other data we may attribute this to individual differences in the temperature level at which positive sweating begins.

Reactions of the Body to a Cold Environment

In the zone of body cooling the primary reaction of the body is a lowering of skin temperature due to constriction of the superficial blood vessels of the skin. Under conditions of long exposure to a chilling atmosphere there would be, as noted above, a compensatory rise in metabolism, generally associated with shivering and with a tendency to move about, beat the arms together and in other ways to increase muscular activity. In our own studies exposure to extreme cold has not been sufficiently prolonged to cause shivering or other muscular movements. As soon, however, as the coolness of the thermal environment falls below a critical value (30° for the semi-reclining nude subject), the skin temperature begins to fall.

In the experiments presented in Figure 7, for example, we may note that above 30° there was a rise in skin temperature, for nude subjects, of 1° for each 4° increase in operative temperature; while below 30° there was a fall of 1° in skin temperature for each fall of 2.9° in operative temperature.

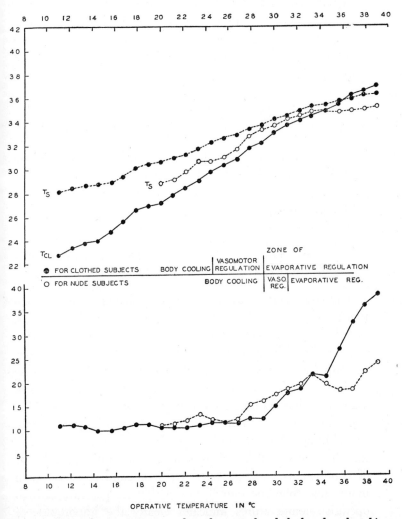

Figure 7. Mean skin temperature and conductance for clothed and nude subjects various Operative Temperatures.

75

We have found it helpful to analyze the influence of this fall in skin temperature upon heat loss in terms of a factor which we have called "conductance." [130] Under cold conditions the total heat flow from the interior of the body to its surface is equal to the difference between metabolism and Heat Change (which will be negative in this case). If we divide this figure by the surface area of the body and divide again by the difference between rectal temperature and skin temperature, we have a measure of heat flux per unit area of skin. In other words,

$$\frac{M - \Delta H}{A(T_R - T_S)} = K \text{ cal.}/\text{m.}^2/°C.$$

The value of conductance (K), determined in this way, shows (for the same nude subject for whom data are presented in Figure 7) the following differences, above and below the critical temperature:

	MINIMUM	MEAN	MAXIMUM
Above 30°	18.0	20.3	23.8
Below 30°	10.6	12.6	15.9

The conductance, as thus recorded, obviously depends on two major factors, thermal conductance of the body tissues, and the flow of blood which brings warm blood to the surface to be cooled. The first of these factors is influenced, however, not only by the specific conductivity of the flesh itself but also by the depth of surface tissues which are actually cooled below a normal value. This gradient is itself influenced to a considerable extent by blood flow, but is also affected by the progressive chilling of deeper and deeper layers of body tissue. The fact that the rate of lowering of skin temperature (and hence of conductance) at low operative temperatures is so much more rapid than the rate of rise in skin temperature at high operative temperatures indicates clearly the importance of vasoconstriction, and the suddenness with which the picture changes at 30° suggests a definite reflex response.

It should be emphasized that quantitative values may vary widely in different subjects. While a very stout subject showed a conductance of 18.3 under warm conditions and a conductance of 12.4 under cold conditions, the corresponding values for a less well-insulated slender subject were 25.0 and 13.7. The second subject, too, showed very high values (K over 35) at extremely high operative temperatures. In both cases, however, there was the same sharp break at 30° operative temperature, obviously indicative of vasoconstriction.

The physiological reactions in this process have been reviewed in some detail elsewhere[38] with reference to the important studies of Kleiber, Burton, Bazett, and Hardy and DuBois. All that need be said here is that below an operative temperature of 28° for both nude and clothed subjects the value of K lies approximately constant between 10 and 12 (with gradients between rectal and skin temperature varying from 4.5° up to 9.5°, as one proceeds to cooler and cooler environments). At operative temperatures over 30°, the K-values rise more or less steadily with higher operative temperatures, reaching 23.8 for the nude and 38.7 for the clothed subjects at an operative temperature of 38.9°. In this area the great increase in conductance is accompanied by progressive reductions in the gradient between rectal and skin temperature (4.5° to 1.5°). Clearly, in the zone of body cooling a maximum vasoconstriction has been reached, and K remains constant. In the zone of evaporative regulation, on the other hand, the relatively rapid rise of conductance must be due chiefly to progressively increasing blood flow. Analysis of the data indicates that, under the critical conditions where there is a minimum K-value and a difference of 4.5° between skin and body temperature, the depth of the tissue layer cooled below the general body temperature is 2.2 cm. The increase in blood flow corresponding to the conductance of 38.9 observed at 39°

operative temperature for the clothed subject indicates an increase in blood volume in the peripheral layers of the body equal to 21 per cent of the normal output of the heart.

The lowering of conductance by vasoconstriction in cold environments and the lowering of skin temperature which accompanies it is a useful adaptive mechanism for reducing the strain put upon the body by such environments. That this mechanism is quite unable to cope effectively with any considerable fall in operative temperature is, however, clear from the rapid increase in the heat loss which is noted below 26° operative temperature with the nude subject, and below 20° with the clothed subject. Clearly, such marked cooling of body tissues could not continue progressively for any extended period without serious interference with bodily functions. Missenard[80] has correctly pointed out that the minimum tolerable environmental temperature should be defined as the lowest temperature at which the body can maintain, *for an indefinite period,* its interior temperature for a given rate of metabolism.

Actual Skin Temperatures for Various Regions of the Body Surface Beyond the Area of Equilibrium

Figure 8 shows the difference in skin temperature for four of the main regions of the body at twenty different operative temperatures, using the mean values for four nude subjects in the usual semi-reclining position.

It will be noted that in the zone of evaporative regulation (at the right of the chart) values for the trunk remain constant (34.9° to 35.2°), and values for the upper extremities also remain constant (34.6° to 34.7°). Values for the head rise slightly with rising environmental temperature in this zone (from 34.8° at operative temperature 32.2° to 35.7° at operative temperature 38.9°). The temperature of the legs also rises from 34.4° at operative temperature of 33.3° to 35.1° at operative temperature of 38.9°.

Below 33° operative temperatures for the lower extremities,

and below 32° operative temperatures for the other three areas, all skin temperatures begin to fall more rapidly as operative temperatures fall (passing toward the left of the chart).

The rate of fall is least rapid with the trunk and most rapid with the lower extremities. The actual temperatures for the four areas at the highest and lowest temperatures employed, with both nude and clothed subjects and at mid-point (33.3°) where active sweat secretion began, are shown on page 80.

It will be noted that at 33.3° operative temperature all four major areas of the nude subjects showed a skin temperature between 34.4° and 34.9°. For the clothed subjects the range at this operative temperature was 34.7° to 35.9°, the head being 1° warmer with clothing.

Above this point of equilibrium, the values for the nude subject rose slightly (less than 1°) on the head and lower extremities. The corresponding increase for the clothed subjects was more considerable (1.1° for the lower extremities and

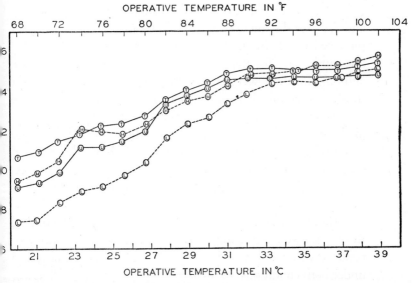

OPERATIVE TEMPERATURE IN °F

Figure 8. Regional variation of skin temperature in a resting nude subject in relation to
tive Temperature. T, H, U, L = trunk, head, upper and lower extremities, respec-

	Operative temperature	Skin temperatures			
		Trunk	Head	Upper extr.	Lower extr.
Nude subjects	38.9	35.2	35.7	34.7	35.1
	33.3	34.9	34.9	34.6	34.4
Difference		.3	.8	.1	.7
	33.3	34.9	34.9	34.6	34.4
	20.0	30.6	29.4	29.1	27.3
Difference		4.3	5.5	5.5	7.1
Clothed subjects	35.9	36.5	37.2	35.9	35.8
	33.3	35.9	35.4	35.0	34.7
Difference		.6	1.8	.9	1.1
	33.3	35.9	35.4	35.0	34.7
	20.0	33.9	32.4	29.4	28.4
Difference		2.0	3.0	5.6	6.3

1.8° for the head). In the zone of body cooling, on the other hand, skin temperatures for the nude subject fell more rapidly (4.3° for the trunk, 5.5° for the head and upper extremities, and 7.1° for the lower extremities). In the case of the subject protected by clothing, the decrease was much less (2.0° for the trunk, 3.0° for the head, 5.6° for the upper extremities, and 6.3° for the lower extremities). In all cases the important trunk temperature is kept constant by vasoconstriction on the extremities. Clothing protects against cold in general, except in the case of the upper extremities, where the fall for nude and clothed subjects is practically identical. In the zone of evaporative regulation, on the other hand, changes are greatest for the clothed subject, particularly in the case of the upper extremities and head.

A similar study with subjects performing vigorous physical work[131] showed surprisingly similar results, so far as skin temperature was concerned. In the case of Subject VII, observed under both conditions, mean skin temperature was 1–2° *lower* when work was performed at a given high operative temperature than at the same operative temperature with the subject at rest; and this difference was apparent for all areas of the body. Such a phenomenon offers striking evidence of the power of evaporative cooling. Rectal temperatures, on the other hand, were nearly 1° higher under working conditions, in natural association with greatly increased metabolism.

The successive points in Figure 8 are for independent experiments made at progressively increasing operative temperatures. Figure 9 shows the progressive changes in skin temperature for various areas (and also changes in superficial clothing

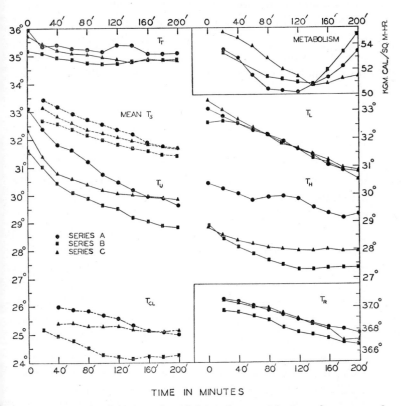

TIME IN MINUTES

Figure 9. Progressive changes in heat balance factors with time of exposure, observed at three different rates of air movement and temperature. Series A, 16.1°C and 4.6 cm./sec.; Series B, 19.2°C and 34 cm./sec.; Series C, 22.7°C and 204 cm./sec. T, trunk, S, mean skin; U, upper extremities; L, lower extremities; H, head; CL, clothing surface; R, rectal.

temperatures and rectal temperatures and metabolism) for the mean of experiments with two clothed subjects after various periods of exposure, at three different rates of air movement. Series A was at an environmental temperature of 16.1° with 4.6 cm./sec. air movement; Series B at 19.2° with 34 cm./sec. air movement; Series C at 22.7° with 204 cm./sec. air movement.[133]

It will be noted that the temperature of the trunk surface fell less than 0.5° and reached an apparently stable value after 120 minutes. The mean temperatures of the head and upper extremities fell more sharply, 1° to 2° in the case of the head and 3° in the case of the upper extremities) and were approaching stability at 200 minutes. These are, of course, the areas, wholly or in part, freely exposed to the air in the clothed subject. The temperature of the lower extremities dropped 1° to 2.5° and showed no sign of approaching stability. The rectal temperature dropped only 0.3° but did not arrive at a stable level in the 200-minute period of the experiments. The mean skin temperature (obtained by giving weights of 7 to the head, 21 to the upper extremities, 31 to the trunk, and 41 to the lower extremities) fell 1° to 2° and did not reach stability.

For simplicity this analysis has been based on the four major regions of the body; but there were, of course, marked differences between the fifteen points at which skin temperature was recorded which fell within a given area. The back of the head was cooler than the forehead and cheek. The back of the hand showed a much lower temperature than the arm, even in the case of the nude subject. The dorsal trunk maintained a rather stable temperature, with the kidney areas cooler than the shoulder blades. The foot cooled much more rapidly than the upper part of the lower extremities.

In an earlier study[136] observations were also made on the reaction of regional skin temperatures to localized drafts of 400 to 1700 feet per minute directed against either the head or the feet of the subject. When the draft was directed on the head, under cold conditions, the skin temperature of the face dropped about 4°, the surface temperature of the nasal mucosa over 5°, the temperature of the feet 1°, and trunk, thigh, and hand temperatures less than 1°. When the draft was directed on the feet, the skin temperature of this area fell 2° to 3°; and the temperature of the nasal mucosa rose 1° to 2°. This is an interesting reflex reaction. Other areas showed no changes of significant magnitude.

Much more extreme deviations of local skin temperature were observed under exceptional conditions. One of the most striking of these is shown in Figure 10. In this experiment two clothed subjects were observed, seated in ordinary straight-backed chairs at an environmental temperature of 20°. For the first half-hour, they were wrapped in blankets to secure a baseline condition of vasodilation. The blankets were removed for one hour and restored for one hour. After this, the blankets were again removed and an ice-bag, covering about 60 square centimeters, was applied to the nape of the neck. After 15 minutes of contact, the ice-bag was removed and the subject remained in the chair (without blankets) for a final hour. Skin temperatures on the chest, upper arm, and side calf all fell appreciably when the blankets were removed in both the control and the experimental period. On these areas, however, the fall during the experimental period of cooling (with the presence of the ice-bag) was less than in the control period of cooling (without the ice-bag). It should naturally be less since the initial temperatures at the time the blanket was removed for the second time were lower than when it was removed for the first time. In any case, the presence of the ice-bag was not registered by these areas. On the other hand, the skin temperature on the tip of the finger was quite unaffected by the removal of the blanket in the control period with Subject VII, and dropped during this period by 6° in the case of Subject IX. In the presence of the ice-bag, however, the finger temperature dropped over 10° in both instances. Furthermore, this decrease went progressively forward for about two hours *after*

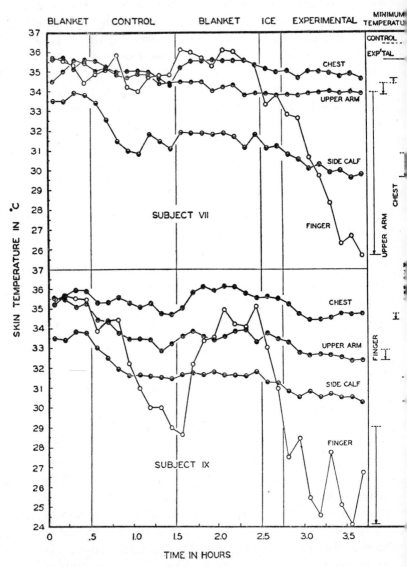

Figure 10. The effect of a cold stimulus on vasomotor control of skin temperatu in skin regions remote from the point of cold application. Ice bag application on sq. cm. of skin (dorsal neck area).

the ice-bag was removed.[142] The vasomotor phenomena involved in such reactions are similar to those produced by local "cold" radiation or drafts.

Equally striking decreases in finger temperatures due to emotional stress have been reported by DuBois.[27] One woman subject, in reading aloud a political speech which aroused an emotional conflict in her mind, showed a fall in finger temperature from over 32° to about 27°. Another subject, who was attempting to solve a difficult problem, was harassed by loud noises and verbal taunts and interruptions. Her finger skin temperature dropped from about 33° to under 24°. It is interesting to note, however, that the vasoconstriction caused in these two instances by emotional disturbance ceased at once after the crisis was passed, and the finger temperature returned almost, but not quite, to normal in 20 minutes, instead of the prolonged progressive influence in our experiments with local chilling.

The power of the body to readjust its equilibrium after temporary disturbance is extraordinary. DuBois[27] cites the case of two subjects who played three games of hard squash rackets in a court at a temperature of 21°C. DuBois estimates that heat production in their bodies was increased twelve-fold by the exercise. Evaporative heat loss was so great that it caused a marked drop in skin temperature; but it was insufficient to take care of the increased metabolism, and the rectal temperature rose to over 39°. Such rises in rectal temperature during exercise are regarded by some physiologists as a regulative effect designed to provide internal temperatures of optimal character for high rates of exercise metabolism. "At the end of the game the players were dripping wet. But after standing quietly for a few minutes in the dressing room, the skin became dry and warm. They lost heat with amazing rapidity, and at the end of 37 minutes the rectal temperatures had returned to normal. One man then took a warm shower followed by a cold shower of one minute, and his skin temperature fell 5° but rose again promptly."

Physiological Adaptations in the Zone of Evaporative Regulation

This episode leads us naturally to consideration of the physiological mechanism involved in adaptation to environmental conditions above the area of thermal equilibrium.

In this region the body, as indicated in Figure 11, has an extraordinarily effective process of compensation for an environment of high heat stress, a compensation which in its physical manifestations is very simple, being accomplished by a progressive increase in evaporation. The perfection of this reaction, however, involves physiological adjustments of considerable complexity.

Under the conditions of ordinary studies of basal metabolism, with reasonably standard conditions of thermal environment, the evaporative heat loss from the body is moderately low and highly constant. DuBois[27] tabulates a large number of experiments of this type for normal persons and those suffering from various diseases, in which the percentage of metabolic heat lost by evaporation varies only between 21 per cent and 28 per cent. Under such conditions, the insensible perspiration bears a direct straight-line relationship to metabolism. The value of 25 per cent for the insensible perspiration in relation to total heat loss has been regarded as an approximation. The extensive studies of Newburgh[93, 94] have shown, however, that the true value for 24-hour periods of normal life routines is quite constant and very close to 25 per cent, averaging 24.4 per cent with a variation of ±0.7 per cent in different subjects. This relation has been used by Newburgh to calculate the total metabolism over 24-hour periods.

Under hot environmental conditions, on the other hand, the evaporative heat loss may rise, as we have seen, to very high values. In one particular series of experiments, with air and walls at 27.9°, the metabolism was 85 calories per man, the heat gain from air and walls was 45 calories, and the evaporative heat lost amounted to 116 calories, or 136 per cent of the metabolic rate. The net heat change of the body was 14 calories.

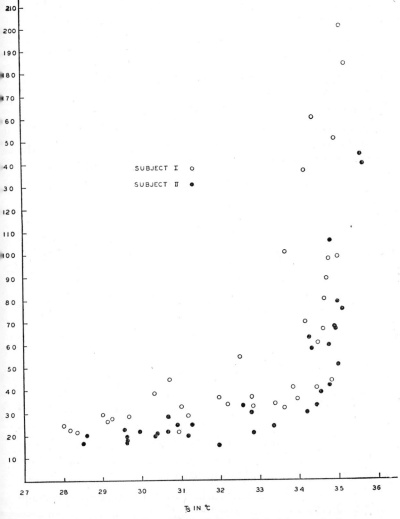

Figure 11. Total evaporative heat loss from the unclothed human body at various in temperatures under conditions of rest.

The obvious environmental factor which is related to the phenomenon of increased sweat secretion is air temperature, but this relationship is only manifest above the critical level of the area of thermal equilibrium. Below an operative temperature of about 30°, with the nude semi-reclining subject, evaporative heat loss is slight (10 to 20 calories per square meter) and varies according to the physical moisture demand of the vapor tension of the atmosphere. Above this point comes a sharp increase. This increase in evaporation is, of course, generally proportionate to progressive increase in air and wall temperature; but it is not governed by physical demands of the atmosphere, since it bears no relation to the relative humidity of the atmosphere in this range. The physical capacity of the air to take up moisture changes enormously at various humidities, as indicated by the table below.

Amount of water that can be retained
by air at various temperatures

Temperature °C	Grams per cubic meter
−20	.9
−10	2.1
0	4.8
10	9.3
20	17.0
30	29.9

Air which is completely saturated at 0°C is only 28 per cent saturated when warmed to 20°. Yet in spite of wide variation in temperature and relative humidity, the actual evaporation from the body, over a very considerable thermal range, is maintained at equilibrium level by a varying rate of secretion of sweat on the body surface in accord with specific adaptive physiological processes.[140]

The best index of the rate of evaporative heat loss is to be found in skin temperature. As indicated in Figure 11, evaporative heat loss remains fairly constant (below 20 calories per square meter) up to a mean skin temperature of 32°. Above this point it rises progressively on a parabolic curve to over 90 calories per square meter at a skin temperature of over 35°. Thus, while in the zone of body cooling evaporation remains relatively constant while skin temperature falls, the reverse is the case in the zone of evaporative regulation. Here the evaporative heat loss, owing to active sweat secretion, increases rapidly and the process is so efficient that a rise of 11° in operative temperature is reflected in a rise in skin temperature of less than 3°.

Each major region of the body shows a critical temperature of its own, corresponding to the general mean skin temperature of 32° at which active sweat secretion (more than 20 calories per square meter) sets in. Sharp acceleration in evaporative cooling appears in every case when the skin of the head exceeds 35.5°, when the skin of the trunk and upper extremities exceeds 34.5°, when the skin of the lower extremities exceeds 33.5°, and when the mean skin temperature of the whole body exceeds 34.5°.[139]

With clothed subjects, the sharp increase in evaporation sets in at a lower operative temperature (24° instead of 30° for the nude subject). The upper limits of evaporative cooling (to be discussed in a later paragraph) are of course more limited by high humidity with the clothed subject.[143]

In analyzing the process of evaporative regulation we have found it convenient to introduce a new physiological concept, analogous to the factor of conductance, used in studying adaptation at lower temperatures.[34]

The evaporation from a liquid surface is proportional to the difference between the vapor pressure of the liquid itself and the vapor pressure of the air in contact with its surface. Actual evaporation equals the difference between these vapor pressures (Δv.p.) multiplied by a factor, μ which varies with the rate of air movement and its direction with regard to the wetted surface. It can, of course, be experimentally determined for a given rate and direction of air movement. The differential of the two vapor pressures multiplied by μ gives us the theoretical evaporation which would occur if the unit area of body surface were covered evenly with moisture.

$$\Delta\text{v.p.} \times \mu = E' \text{ (theoretical evaporation)}.$$

If we subtract evaporation from the respiratory passages to the respired air, the ratio of actual evaporation, E, to this theoretical evaporation, E', gives us a measure of the extent to which the unit area of body surface is actually saturated with moisture. This ratio we call Wetted Area, and express as a percentage, thus:

$$\text{w.a.} = \frac{E}{\Delta\text{v.p.} \times \mu} \times 100 \text{ per cent.}$$

The maximum value of this ratio, with complete saturation of skin surface would, of course, be 100. When actual observed evaporation exceeds the theoretical value (E'), as it has done in certain experiments with clothed subjects, it seems certain that water is running off without evaporation or is being evaporated from the surfaces of the clothing in such a way that the full cooling effect of the evaporation is not actually obtained.

Our experiments indicate that for the nude subject the maximum limiting value of E' is close to 30 calories per square meter of body surface per hour for each centimeter of mercury pressure difference.[34, 143] This figure applies only to turbulent air velocities of 15 feet per minute or less, such as obtain in an ordinary indoor space and such as were maintained in our basic experiments. It corresponds closely with data obtained by Carrier and other engineers who have studied the physical factors in evaporation from liquid surfaces.

Values for Wetted Area computed in this way for two nude

subjects were as follows (in percentage, 30 calories assumed as 100 per cent):

	Operative temperature	Subject I		Subject II	
		No. expt.	w.a. %	No. expt.	w.a. %
Maximum	40.5–41.0°	1	96	1	95
Mean	Over 34°	9	64	8	62
Mean	30–34°	8	24	8	27
Mean	Under 34°	18	13	19	13
Minimum	18°	1	1	1	1

Thus, under extremely hot conditions the actual amount of evaporation closely approaches what it would be if the body surface were completely covered with moisture. Under very cold conditions the actual evaporation was only 1 per cent of the assumed possible value. Below 30° operative temperature, the value remains very low. At 30° it begins to rise a trifle more rapidly and at about 34° it increases very sharply, as indicated in Figure 11.

The exactness of our assumed maximum value of 30 (on which the figures above are computed as percentages) cannot affect the relative results obtained, and it cannot be far from the truth in view of special studies made by us at extreme conditions. Of course it can apply only to the low turbulent air movements studied. Higher maxima are obtained with high air velocity. In studies with subjects performing active work by pedaling on a stationary bicycle[131] at high operative temperatures we have observed values of 67 calories for evaporative heat loss per centimeter of Hg vapor pressure difference. The effect of pedaling rapidly is, of course, the same as that of greatly increased air movement. When called upon to estimate the increase in the factor of 30 for higher air movements we have generally multiplied this limit by the ratio of

the convection constant at the basal air movement of our ex
periments to its value for the new air movement. This factor
requires further experimental investigation.

Under constant conditions of low air movement, however,
the value of w.a. seems clearly to represent the actual determining factor in evaporative heat loss at high temperatures.
This factor, and not the relative humidity of the atmosphere,
is what actually governs the rate of evaporation from the skin
surface under hot conditions. It is due to physiological reactions of the body governing the rate of sweat secretion and not
to mere spreading of sweat over the surface.[143] Obviously it
cannot be assumed that a w.a.-ratio of 50 per cent means that
half the body is covered with sweat and half is not. Actually
the various areas of skin surface differ widely in their concentration of sweat glands. DuBois cites Benedict and Ward-
law to the effect that 30 per cent of evaporative loss from the
skin comes from the hands and feet, which represent only 12
per cent of the total skin area; and he quotes the statement by
Kuno and Ikenchi that the hands and feet vaporize ten times
as fast as certain other areas. Wetted Area, however, appears
to be a reliable measure of the extent of the adaptation of the
sweat secreting mechanism to hot conditions.

DuBois[27] has shown that under otherwise constant conditions evaporative heat loss bears a straight-line relationship to
metabolism, another instance of the adaptive nature of this
mechanism. Our studies have indicated,[140] as would be expected, that it bears a close relationship to conductance (see
Figure 12), both rising at a given operative temperature much
more sharply under the smaller differences of vapor pressure
which obtain with high atmospheric humidity.

The trigger mechanism which activates the sweat stimulating mechanism begins to act, with nude semi-reclining subjects, at an operative temperature of 30°. For the clothed
subject in moist air, active increase in sweat secretion sets in
at 25°.[143] Under conditions of active physical work, it begins
at 20°.

It seems clear, as indicated in Figure 13, that the onset of active sweat secretion is closely related to both skin temperature and rectal temperature. For both clothed and nude sub-

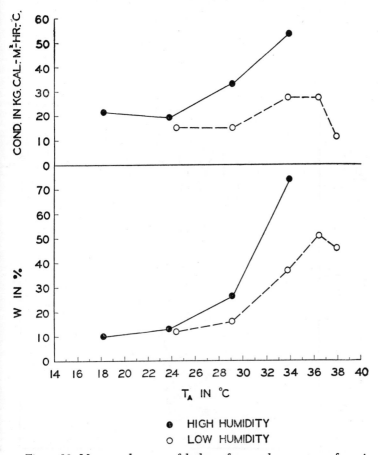

Figure 12. Mean conductance of body surfaces and percentage of maximum possible area of wetted skin surface in relation to air temperature (for all subjects studied under corresponding conditions).

jects, the sharp rise in w.a. comes when the mean skin temperature reaches 35° and when the rectal temperature exceeds 37.2°. That both skin and rectal temperatures must play a part is indicated by the fact that in experiments with nude resting

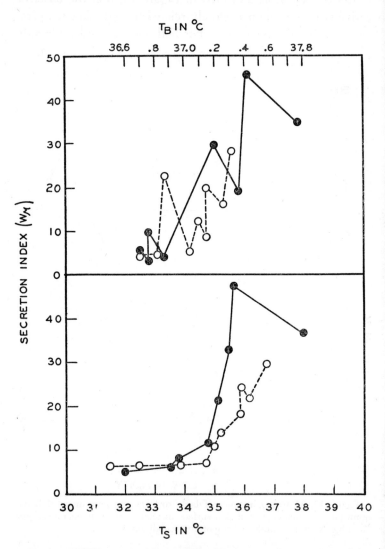

Figure 13. Relation of secretion index (W_μ) to rectal temperature (T_B) and skin temperature (T_S) for clothed subjects. Open circles for low humidity, closed circles for high humidity.

subjects[140] we often observed very high evaporation with high skin temperatures, even when rectal temperatures were below 37°; while in experiments with working subjects[131] we observed high evaporation with high rectal temperatures, even when skin temperatures were kept low by high evaporation.

The complexity of the physiological mechanism involved is indicated by the fact that it shows a clearly marked seasonal adaptation. Two subjects, observed under conditions of active physical work, who showed the onset of active sweat secretion at 20° in winter, began to secrete actively in summer at a temperature several degrees lower. In this case the additional air movement produced by pedaling movements made possible evaporation at a rate higher than our basic figure of 30 calories per square meter per hour per centimeter of mercury vapor pressure difference. The actual figures recorded were as follows for the mean of two subjects in 30 experiments.

Operative temperature C°	12–16°	16–19°	20–23°
Evaporation in calories per square meter per hour per cm. Hg.			
Winter	11.5	10.2	16.1
Summer	11.3	32.6	35.8

At operative temperatures between 16° and 19° the rate of sweat secretion was three times as great for the same subjects under the same conditions in winter as in summer, and even between 20° and 23° it was still twice as great. It is the lack of this adaptation of the sweat-secreting mechanism which makes the first hot days in spring so much more uncomfortable than similar days later in the summer.

How far adaptive adjustment to low temperatures can be acquired has not been clearly demonstrated in the case of man. Missenard[80] cites the researches of Gelineo which showed that rats which had been acclimatized to a temperature of 0° to 2° showed a basal metabolism of 38 calories per square meter per hour and a maximum metabolism of over 129 calories, as compared with a basal figure of 23 calories and a maximum of 63 calories for rats which had been acclimatized to a temperature of 30° to 32°. The temperature at which an adaptive rise in metabolism set in was also greatly decreased by cold adaptation.

The Upper Limits of Evaporative Regulation

Precise and effective as the process of evaporative regulation is, it operates only within certain defined limits. The most important limiting factor is the amount of moisture which the atmosphere can actually absorb from a saturated surface. If we assume a maximum wetted area and a skin temperature of 35.6°, we can compute for any combination of atmospheric temperature and humidity the number of calories per unit area of skin which will be actually evaporated (Δv.p. $\times$ 30 calories). Knowing the constants for convection and radiation, as determined by methods outlined in Chapter II, and assuming a metabolic rate of 47, we can compute the amount of heat which must be given off by evaporation to maintain equilibrium. Any combination of atmospheric temperature and humidity, beyond which the possible heat loss by evaporation does not equal the evaporative heat loss necessary for equilibrium, lies beyond the upper limit of tolerance.[140] With saturated air at any temperature, evaporation is of course zero, except for the usually small differential in vapor pressure represented by the difference in the saturation values for air and mean skin temperatures, and tolerance is reached when radiative and convective heat loss equal metabolism.

The upper limits for four rates of air movement are shown in Figure 14 for a nude subject at rest. It will be noted that below air temperatures of about 35°, with high humidities, increase in air velocity always widens the zone of evaporative regulation. In hotter atmospheres with lower humidities, however, increased air movement not only increases evaporative heat loss, but also increases heat gain from the environment by convection. Thus, in the area of the curve, the limits of tolerance are higher with relatively still air (17 feet per minute) than with velocities of 30 or 100 feet per minute.

Clothing also broadens the zone of evaporative regulation by increasing effective evaporative surface and by protecting the

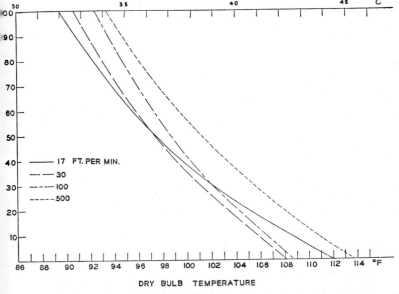

Figure 14. Contour chart indicating upper limits (wetted area = 100%) of zone of evaporative regulation for various air velocities.

body against heat gain from the environment by radiation and convection. The figures in the table on page 98 illustrate this point.[37]

When the upper limits of evaporative regulation are reached, disastrous consequences ensue. With our clothed subjects, profound discomfort was manifest with high relative humidity (70 to 80 per cent) even at atmospheres between 37° and 39°, and some subjects showed nausea and other subjective symptoms so severe that the experiments had to be discontinued. Under such conditions skin temperatures and rectal temperatures begin to rise sharply and, what is even more serious, metabolism rises also, thus creating a vicious spiral.

The data obtained in our laboratory correspond well with the findings of McConnell, Houghten, and Yaglou[77] that saturated air at 32.2° is the "upper limit of man's ability to

Upper limits of evaporative regulation

Environmental temperature	Relative humidity	
	Clothed subject	Nude subject
52.7	0	
50.0	5	
45.0	18	1
42.5	26	13
40.0	38	29
37.5	51	47
35.0	69	70
32.5	89	100
31.0	100	

compensate for atmospheric conditions" in still air. They are also in accord with the reports of Cadman and Haldane.[23] Cadman states that at 29.4° wet-bulb temperature the body temperature invariably rises, while at 33.9° wet-bulb "one is in a terrible state"; Haldane states that at 31 to 32° wet-bulb "in fairly still air, the body temperature begins to rise, even in the case of persons stripped to the waist and doing no work; and when air is saturated this rise continues until symptoms of heat stroke arise."

These effects are not, of course, instantaneous. The Pittsburgh investigators found exceptional subjects who could endure such extreme conditions as 70°C with a relative humidity of 15 per cent for half an hour. The body temperature under such conditions rose several degrees. The pulse rate seemed to be the best measure of sensation, 135 beats per minute corresponding to marked discomfort, and pulse rates exceeding 150 being almost unbearable. Restlessness, irritability, headache, and palpitation of the heart, soreness of the eyes, a severe oppression of the chest, dizziness and confusion were among the sensations experienced; and weakness and a dragged-out feeling persisted for some time after such experiments had closed.

Under such conditions of very active sweating, the body, of course, suffers from water loss and, in even more serious degree, from loss of sodium chloride. It is, therefore, the custom to provide salt tablets for men who do heavy work under such conditions. The same procedure was followed during the war with troops in the tropics.

In the early days of steam, temperatures in the furnace rooms of naval vessels in the tropics sometimes passed 65°C, with high relative humidity. In 1909 and 1910 the attack rate for heat stroke in the Navy was about 8 per 1000, and between 1861 and 1911, there were 20 deaths and 33 men invalided from this cause. Severe cramps and muscle twitchings attributed to local drying-out of the tissues and accumulation of waste products of metabolism are among the pronounced symptoms of heat stroke, and the body temperature may be so completely upset that temperatures of 104° to 117°F have been recorded.

Under ordinary conditions of indoor life, where air temperatures are not extremely high but relative humidity may often be considerable, the upper limit of thermal adaptation is established by the physical capacity of the atmosphere to take up moisture from the skin, as illustrated in Figure 14. In a very hot and dry atmosphere, such as one finds in some desert regions, another factor comes into play—the physiological capacity of the body to produce sweat. In such an atmosphere the difference of vapor pressure between skin and air is so great that, even with maximum vasodilation, the sweat glands are unable to maintain a high wetted area. This phenomenon is illustrated in Figure 15.[128]

The three curves in this figure indicate the upper limits of tolerance fixed by the evaporative power of the atmosphere for nude subjects under three conditions. Curve A is for a

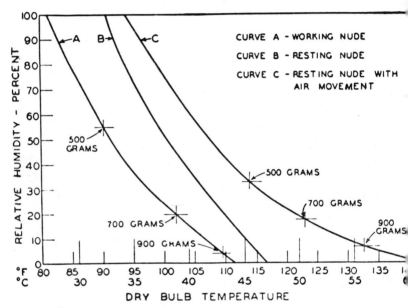

Figure 15. Upper limits of evaporative regulation. Curve A, working: heat production 425 cal./hr., air movement 15 ft./min. Curve B, resting: 85 cal./hr., air movement 15 ft./min. Curve C, resting: 85 cal./hr., air movement 100 ft./min. Crosses indicate points on limits which can be reached through the indicated evaporative water loss in grams per hour.

subject at work with a total heat production of 425 calories per hour and minimal air movement; curve B is for a subject at rest with a total metabolism of 85 calories at minimal air movement; C for a resting subject exposed to air movement at a rate of 100 feet per minute. The crosses on curves A and C indicate the upper limit of tolerance which would be set by the physiological capacity of the body to produce certain stated amounts of sweat (500, 700, and 900 grams per hour).

At a temperature of 27°C both resting and working subjects can adjust in still air even at 100 per cent relative humidity. The resting subject can also adjust with any relative humidity at 32° and the resting subject in rapidly moving air (100 feet per minute) can adjust with any humidity up to 35°. The general slope of the lines below these points indicates the limits of possible adjustment based on the absorptive capacity of the atmosphere. The resting nude can, of course, adapt to much more extreme conditions than the working subject, and the zone of adaptation is further broadened by a high degree of air movement (100 feet per minute).

In curve A of Figure 15 it will be noted that at 32°C the upper limit for the working subject is at 55 per cent relative humidity; if this line were continued downward and to the right on a basis of atmospheric absorptive power, the working subject would adjust to 39° and 20 per cent relative humidity, and to 43° and 3 per cent relative humidity. In this area, however, the other limiting factor, the power of the body to produce sweat, comes into the picture. In this respect individuals vary widely, and the same individual may greatly increase his ability to secrete sweat. Dill [24] has shown that a subject working in hot dry desert air can double his capacity for moisture production, by practice, from 600 grams to 1200 grams per hour (from a little over a pint of water to a little more than a quart). In football games even higher figures have been recorded. If, however, we assume a representative figure for the normal individual, approximating Dill's initial value, it is found that above 32° the working subject would not be able to produce the amount of moisture necessary for adjustment, even though the atmosphere could absorb it. For the working subject producing 700 grams of moisture, this limit of secreting power would come at 39°, and for the subject secreting 900 grams at 43°. Vertical lines drawn downward on the graph would indicate these limits, and similar limits are set for the resting nude in moving air; for the subject producing 500 grams at 46°, for the subject producing 700 grams at 51°, and for the subject producing 900 grams at 56°. At any point below the slope of the graph and to the left of the appropriate vertical line, the subject can maintain thermal balance. Above the slope and to the right of the vertical line, adaptation is no longer possible.

The general topic of adjustment to extreme heat and cold has been the subject of many excellent studies within the past few years. The relations noted above have been investigated for a number of different conditions of exercise, clothing, and type of climatic exposure. Many of these studies grew out of military interests of the recent war period. This has a bearing on the use of such concepts as limit and tolerance in relation to human climatic endurance. Neither term is susceptible of exact definition since human motivation inevitably enters in the practical testing of such concepts. In general the limits suggested by our work as reported in the foregoing discussions are conservative. Interested readers will find in the studies of Belding, Russell, and Darling,[9] of Eichna, Bean, Ashe, and Nelson,[30] and Robinson, Turrell, and Gerking[110] important and highly useful investigations of the thermal adjustment of man to a variety of working loads under both hot and cold climatic stress. Taylor and Marbarger[122] have extended this work to include a special treatment of tolerance times in environments in which ultimate adjustment is not possible. Our work is not immediately concerned with these more extreme conditions, but the discussion here would be incomplete without indicating the extent to which recent work has extended our range of knowledge concerning human reactions to the more severe exposures.

These experimental approaches to the problem of human tolerance to high heat stress have been critically reviewed in two highly informative articles by the English meteorologist, David Brunt.[14, 16] In his second article Brunt has developed an equation from which the limiting conditions of thermal equilibrium for men working under high heat stress have been computed. By expressing the heat exchange of the body in two terms, one term representing radiation exchanges and the second term a combination of convection and humidity effects, he defines the heat balance of the body, in the limiting conditions in which body temperature can remain steady (net Heat Change $\Delta H = 0$), as

$$T_s - T_r = \frac{M}{3.6} - \frac{66.7}{3.6} \sqrt{V} (I_s - I_W).$$

This is derived from an equation of more familiar arrangement:

$$M = 3.6 (T_s - T_r) + 66.7 \sqrt{V} (I_s - I_W), \text{ where } \Delta H = 0.$$

A basic similarity in heat exchange by convection and evaporation is assumed in this treatment, and the possibilities of heat loss by convection and evaporation are combined by considering the total heat content of air saturated at the skin temperature (T_s, I_s) and at the wet-bulb temperature (heat content of air saturated at wet-bulb = I_W). The temperature of the dry-bulb does not enter directly, but indirectly through the term T_r (temperature of radiating surfaces), and the limits are computed with the assumption that air temperature equals T_r. Values for I_s and I_W for a series of wet-bulb temperatures are extracted from tables, and the computation of T_r (walls and air being equal) is readily made. By repeating this for a series of values for wet-bulb temperature, it is possible to draw a curve defining the limiting conditions for any assumed value of M and V.

Relation of Thermal Conditions to Human Comfort

Even within the range of reasonably perfect thermal adaptation, and long before extreme strains occur, there are certain

103

definite physiological changes which may have significant effects on human comfort. The basic studies of the New York State Commission, nearly a quarter of a century ago, yielded the following results.

The rectal temperature, when subjects come to the laboratory in the morning, showed a definite relation to the outdoor temperature of the preceding night in the summer season (but not under the artificial conditions of winter life in heated houses). The mean rectal temperature, after 4–8 hours exposure to experimental conditions (subjects normally clothed with moderate activity) was as follows:[95]

Air temperature C°	20°	24°	30°
Relative humidity	50%	50%	80%
Rectal temperature	36.7°	37.0°	37.4°

No difference in blood pressure was noted as between the three atmospheric conditions defined above. A special experiment at 38°C with 87 per cent relative humidity showed a definite increase in systolic pressure. A comparison of changes in diastolic pressure with changes in pulse rate-pulse pressure product showed that the resistance in the peripheral portion of the circulatory system was decreased in the warmer conditions.

Especially interesting results were obtained with regard to one factor, the Crampton Index, which has been neglected in recent years but which is useful as a measure of the efficiency of cardiac and circulatory adjustments to various stresses. This index is based on the ratio between increase in heart rate and rise or fall of blood pressure when the subject passes from a reclining to a standing position. It essentially measures the effectiveness and economy of adaptation to the extra burden of erect posture and is presumably a function of vasomotor reaction. The scale on which the Crampton Index is expressed is so designed that a figure of 100 corresponds to an increase of 10 millimeters of blood pressure with an increase of less than 4 beats in the heart rate; a value of 0 corresponds to a decrease of 10 millimeters of blood pressure with an increase of over 40 in heart beat. The following values were recorded in the Commission experiments.

Air temperature C°	20°	24°	30°
Relative humidity	50%	50%	80%
Crampton Index	60	45	34

Since such substantial variations in physiological status occur, it is to be expected that hot conditions, well within the range of thermal equilibrium, may be accompanied by sensations of discomfort.

The fundamental studies on this latter point were made at the Research Laboratories of the American Society of Heating and Ventilating Engineers (to which full reference will be found in the current issues of the *A.S.H.V.E. Guide*[2]). These tests were based primarily on indications of preference expressed by subjects passing from one carefully regulated room to another room with slightly different temperature or humidity. The major result of these studies was the development of what is known as the Effective Temperature Index. This index was determined for clothed subjects not engaged in active physical work and exposed to minimal air movement (15 to 25 feet per minute). It represents, for these conditions, the net effect upon comfort of variations in atmospheric temperature and humidity. The "effective temperature" is defined as that temperature of completely saturated air which will produce the same subjective sensation of comfort as the particular combination of temperature and humidity observed (in both

Air temperatures, °C, producing equivalent sensations of comfort, with varying degrees of relative humidity and air movement

Relative	Rate of air movement, feet per minute			
humidity (%)	Minimal	100	300	700
20	20.2	21.4	23.3	25.0
50	19.2	20.3	22.5	24.2
100	17.2	18.6	20.8	22.8

cases with minimal air movement). Similar charts have been drawn for higher air velocities; and the way in which the scale works is illustrated in the table (p. 105), showing various combinations of air conditions all producing an effective temperature of 17.2°.

Figure 16, reproduced through the courtesy of the A.S.H.V.E., shows the basic Psychometric Chart prepared by the Society, from which relative humidity and effective temperature can be read off for any combination of dry-bulb and wet-bulb temperatures (in Fahrenheit degrees), for the ordinary indoor condition of minimal air movement.

Figure 17, also reproduced by the courtesy of the A.S.H.V.E., shows the zones of dry-bulb and wet-bulb temperatures cor-

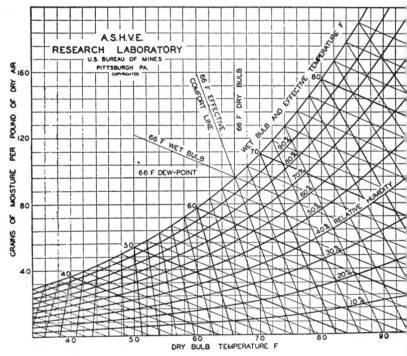

Figure 16. Psychometric chart, persons at rest, normally clothed, in still air. (Reproduced through the courtesy of the American Society of Heating and Ventilating Engineers.)

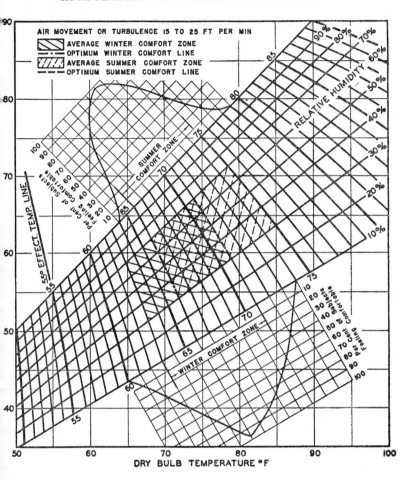

Figure 17. A.S.H.V.E. comfort chart for still air. Both summer and winter comfort zones apply to inhabitants of the United States only. Application of winter comfort line is further limited to rooms heated by central station systems of the convection type. The line does not apply to rooms heated by radiant methods. Application of the summer comfort line is limited to homes, offices, and the like, where the occupants become fully adapted to the artificial air conditions. The line does not apply to theaters, department stores, and the like, where exposure is less than three hours. The optimum summer comfort line shown pertains to Pittsburgh and to other cities in the northern part of the United States and Southern Canada, at elevations not in excess of 1000 feet above sea level. An increase of approximately 1° E.T. should be made for each 5° reduction in north latitude. (Reproduced by courtesy of the American Society of Heating and Ventilating Engineers.)

responding to maximum comfort as determined in the Pittsburgh studies. It will be noted that two separate zones are indicated for winter and for summer comfort, respectively, since it was found that the subjects in the summer preferred distinctly higher temperatures than in winter. The winter comfort zone extends from an effective temperature of 63°F (17.2°C) to one of 71°F (21.7°C). The summer comfort zone ranges between 66°F (18.9°C) and 75°F (23.9°C). An optimal area for all seasons is indicated between 66° and 71°F (18.9° and 21.7°C) with relative humidities between 30 and 70 per cent.

The effective temperature data were obtained in rooms with air and walls at approximately the same temperature. Later A.S.H.V.E. studies have led to the conclusion that an elevation or lowering of the mean radiant temperature of the enclosure 1° above or below the air temperature can be balanced by a 0.5° lowering or raising of effective temperature. The relation of mean radiant temperature to effective temperature can obviously not be a constant one, since it involves evaporative heat loss which is unaffected by radiant temperature. The relative influence of air and wall temperatures can be evalu-

	Men at rest		Men at work, 90,000 ft.-lbs./hr.	
Effective temperature °C	Rise in rectal temp/hr. °C	Increase in pulse rate, beats/min. per hour	Rise in rectal temp/hr. °C	Increase in pulse rate, beats/min. per hour
29.4	.06	1	.33	17
32.2	.17	4	.66	31
35.0	.51	15	1.3	61
38.8	1.2	40	2.2*	103
40.6	2.2	83	3.3*	158
43.3	3.3*	137	4.7*	237

* Computed from exposures lasting less than one hour.

ated only by the factor of operative temperature as defined in Chapter II. It would be much sounder to determine operative temperature directly and then apply it (in place of air temperature) in the Comfort Chart.

A.S.H.V.E. studies[2] on both resting and working subjects (page 108) have shown striking effects of high effective temperature on rectal temperature and pulse rate.

It should be mentioned here that the A.S.H.V.E. effective temperature scale is now in the process of being revised and also extended in scope. It has been realized for some time that the scale provides a very satisfactory index of equivalent conditions at dry-bulb temperatures above approximately 27°. In the lower comfort range, the scale likewise serves to equate the equivalent sensation effects of humidity and temperature for contrast situations in which a person passes from a moderate dry-bulb atmosphere to a similar temperature at high (or low) humidity. After adaptation over a period of one to two hours, however, the sensations realized are not in complete accordance with the scale. In this moderate temperature range (20° to 27°) the effect of humidity is overemphasized.

Work now in progress under the Society's direction will probably result in two scales. One of these, the familiar effective temperature scale in present use, will quite possibly be restricted to use in situations where traffic in and out of conditioned spaces places a premium on short-period contrast sensations. It is expected that to this will be added a similar scale for equilibrium conditions applicable to the comfort-conditioning of spaces with relatively long periods of occupancy. This added equilibrium scale will probably base its equivalent combinations of dry-bulb temperature and relative humidity on lines of equal skin temperature, experimentally determined by methods similar to those which we have developed in connection with partitional calorimetry.

Our studies on comfort in New Haven have been conducted in a somewhat different fashion. Instead of recording impressions of pleasantness on passing from one atmospheric condition to another, we have recorded, for each subject in each experiment, his sensations as recorded by a Comfort Vote on a five-point scale, as follows: (1) very pleasant; (2) pleasant; (3) indifferent; (4) unpleasant; (5) very unpleasant. Votes of (1) and (5) were rare under the conditions listed in the table on page 111.[141]

Discomfort was manifest, both above and below 32° and 34° skin temperature. It might be expected that discomfort would be experienced below 27°, since here the body is experiencing marked negative Heat Change. Above 30°, however, and even up to as high as 40°, the body is in perfect thermal balance as a result of increased evaporative heat loss. Yet in spite of this general thermal balance, the process of

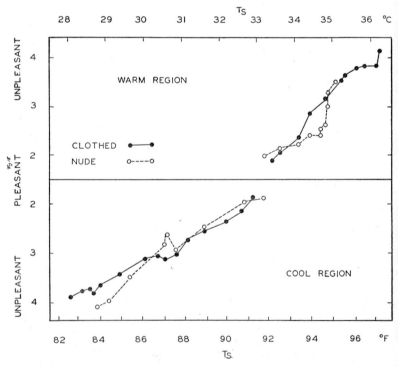

Figure 18. Sensations of pleasantness associated with skin temperature of clothed and nude subjects.

adaptation to hot conditions is evidently accompanied by a marked sense of discomfort.

The correlation of comfort votes with skin temperature (Figure 18) was very close.

Skin temp., °C	No. of expt.	Heat Change, cal./sq. m./hr.	Wetted area, %	Comfort vote
27.8–28.8	5	−39	11	4.5
28.9–29.9	11	−41	11	3.7
30.0–31.0	10	−30	16	2.7
31.1–32.1	13	−32	12	2.6
32.2–33.2	15	−26	16	2.4
33.3–34.3	18	−1	35	2.4
34.4–35.5	36	−3	43	2.7
35.6–36.6	15	−10	59	3.7

We note minimum values for the comfort vote (which means pleasant to indifferent conditions) in the median range of skin temperatures, 32.2° to 34.3°. Above a skin temperature of 34.4°, wetted area increases and the votes begin to rise, averaging between indifferent and unpleasant with skin temperatures above 35.6°. Below a skin temperature of 32.1° the comfort vote also rises, being indifferent or unpleasant below a skin temperature of 29.9° and between unpleasant and very unpleasant below a skin temperature of 28.8°.

The relation of skin temperature to comfort in the cold zone was very close, showing a correlation of −0.64 ±0.09. Marked discomfort (votes over 3.0) began to be experienced when the mean skin temperature fell below 30°, the head temperature below 32°, the trunk temperature below 31°, the upper extremities below 30°, and the lower extremities below 29°. It is of interest to note that in the area of low comfort votes, there may be a moderate degree of negative Heat Change. Chilling of the body tissues to an extent of 25 calories per square meter per hour seems compatible with a sensation of

111

pleasantness for an hour or two, although it could obviously not be borne indefinitely.

On the hot side, three factors—skin temperature, wetted area, and sensation of comfort—are all significantly related, showing primary correlations between 0.50 and 0.65 with standard deviations of 0.06 to 0.08.

Later studies[2] showed that the relation of skin temperature to comfort is close and is identical for both nude and clothed subjects, as indicated in Figure 18, whereas the clothed subjects recorded much higher votes (greater discomfort) for a given evaporative rate than did the nude subjects. Skin temperature seems, therefore, to be the primary factor in the sensation of thermal comfort.

With subjects performing vigorous physical work (metabolism over 300 calories per hour per man),[38] a comfort vote of a different sort was taken. We used a scale on which (1) was very cold; (2) was cool; (3) indifferent; (4) warm; (5) hot. At operative temperatures below 15° to 16°, the subjects were too cold; and at operative temperatures above 16° to 17° they were always too warm. The optimum, then, was at 16° to 17° as compared with 28° for the resting subject. The skin temperature corresponding to the ideal was also lower than for the resting subject. We have noted that for the resting nude subject the skin temperature corresponding to maximum comfort was about 33.5°. With working subjects it was about 29.5°. This is reasonable, since with the working subject the deeper tissues were at a higher temperature than in the case of the resting subject. It does show, however, that under conditions of active work something more than skin temperature alone enters into the picture.

The general relations of sensations of comfort are presented graphically in Figure 19, plotted on the abscissa against dry-bulb temperature and on the ordinate against air movement in the cool zone and against relative humidity in the hot zone.

It should be remembered that Figure 19 applies to nude subjects in a semi-reclining position. The comfort chart of the

A.S.H.V.E. was based on studies with subjects who were allowed a certain freedom of movement and had a substantially higher metabolism. They were fully clothed under cold conditions and stripped to the waist under hot conditions.

Some Problems of the Future

There are many problems to be solved before our knowledge in this field of physiology is in any sense complete.

In the first place, nearly all the studies of reactions to the thermal environment have been made with young adult male subjects. The most important exception is the study of sex difference by Hardy and DuBois.[50] These investigators observed male and female subjects, nude and in a completely reclining position at various operative temperatures. The rectal temperatures of the sexes were the same for comparable conditions, but the following major differences were noted:

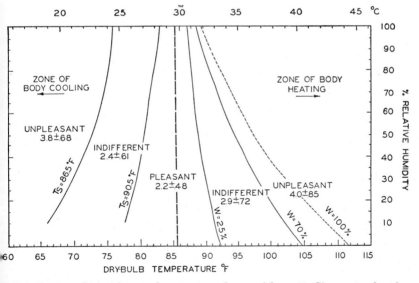

re 19. Contour chart indicating limiting wetted areas (above 30°C) associated with sensations of pleasantness (in the zone of evaporative regulation) in relation to air ature and relative humidity. Observed mean comfort votes indicated in each region. 30°C the chart indicates limiting skin temperatures associated with certain sensations santness.

113

1. The conductance of the skin was throughout less for the women than for the men. This fact is, of course, due to greater thickness of subcutaneous tissues which Hardy and DuBois compute as equal to the effect of a layer of fat about 4 mm. thick.

2. Largely as a result of this difference in conductance, the skin temperatures of the women were 1.0° lower in the cold zone and 1.7° higher in the hot zone than those of the men.

3. As a result of the lower conductance and lower skin temperature, heat loss for women in the cold zone was 10 per cent lower than that for men.

4. The most remarkable difference exhibited was a compensatory fall in metabolic rate for women at an operative temperature above 27°C. This was so marked that, in the hot zone, the metabolism of the women fell 14–20 per cent below that of the men.

5. As a result of the higher skin temperature and lower metabolism, heat loss for women in the hot zone was 14 to 20 per cent lower than for men. The women did not begin to show active sweat secretion until air temperature reached 32° to 33°, while the men began rapid vaporization at 29°.

6. The net result of all this was that the region of thermal adjustment (without active sweat secretion) was only about 2° to 3° for men and 6° for women.

These results are of great significance, and such studies should be extended. (Hardy and DuBois observed only seven women subjects, of whom one failed to show the compensatory decrease in metabolism.) We need similar studies at different age periods, and studies of specific individual differences in thermal adjustment. It is common knowledge that some people thrive on hot summer weather and some are at their best only in the cold season. The physiological basis for such preferences should be of interest. The thermal adjustments of individuals suffering from various diseases might be found to have fundamental significance. The physiological processes involved in seasonal adaptation should also be studied.

Finally, we know almost nothing of the influence upon the body of exposure to conditions which involve marked irregularities in heat loss (or gain) affecting particular areas of the body surface. Has the Englishman who experiences (or thinks he experiences) maximum comfort when one side of his body is chilled by cold air and the other side toasted by radiant heat from an open fire any sound physiological basis for his preference? How serious is the effect of local drafts on various areas of the body? What is the effect of such pronounced local chilling as that shown in Figure 10? What is the reason for the sense of euphoria experienced on a mountain top, with cold air and high air movement combined with hot radiation?

These, and many other questions, challenge the students of thermal physiology in the future.

C H A P T E R I V

THE THERMAL PROTECTIVE
INFLUENCE OF CLOTHING

Protective Functions of Clothing

ETHNOLOGISTS are by no means agreed as to the urges which originally led to the custom of clothing the human body. Shulman[116] cites three groups of authorities who attribute the practice respectively to the desire to attract attention (sexually, or to emphasize prestige), to modesty (the fig-leaf theory of the Garden of Eden), or to the need for environmental protection (against climatic conditions, or brambles and thorns, or bites of insects). Neither of these last two objectives would seem to be met by many of the forms of primitive clothing with which we are familiar. In our present civilized life, all these motives are operative in greater or less degree; but protection against unfavorable atmospheric conditions is certainly a primary essential. We are interested only in this factor in the present discussion.

Methods of Studying the Thermal Influence of Clothing

As we have indicated in preceding chapters, there has long been a considerable body of information on the temperature regulation of the nude human body under moderate thermal stress. Studies of both the physiological and biophysical factors in temperature adjustment date essentially from the time of Rubner, with a particular concentration of activity in the period from 1930–1939, excluding the war years. In this literature, however, only a few studies dealt with the influence

116

of clothing on heat loss. Three reports[62, 63, 76] from the Laboratory of the American Society of Heating and Ventilating Engineers had demonstrated the effect of normal and partial clothing on the sensations of comfort or tolerance to be expected in relation to given effective temperature conditions. Three reports from the John B. Pierce Laboratory[133, 38, 143] and one from the Russell Sage Institute of Pathology[51] had presented analyses of the effect of air movement, humidity, radiation, and convection effects on clothed human subjects in the range from 16°C to 38°C. The latter four studies computed for the first time the insulation value of clothing assemblies. They also demonstrated for the first time the quantitative changes in temperature gradients, circulation, and evaporation loss that occur when the body is exposed in the clothed state. Suddenly, in 1940 and 1941, physiologists were flooded with requests from military authorities for practical information on the heat exchange properties of clothing, and the critical nature of these problems may be estimated from a survey of a few typical questions:

(1) A gunner is to be exposed for several hours in an unheated aircraft gun turret at a temperature of −30°C. His heat production is only slightly above that of a resting man. Three sets of protective clothing are available. The operational inconvenience of these may be roughly summarized in terms of total weights for the three sets—12, 16, and 19 pounds. For how long a period can the man remain efficient in each of these outfits?

(2) A light assembly, weighing 10 pounds, is available for an exposure of −30°C. X watts of electrical energy are available to compensate for reduced insulation. What is the time tolerance of a resting man with such an assembly? Should the electrical heat input be distributed uniformly throughout the assembly, or should the trunk and extremities receive different proportions, depending upon the larger surface per unit of volume in hands and feet? Is it true that the regulation of body temperature is inefficient when the hands are kept lo-

cally comfortable despite a gradual overall cooling of the body system?

(3) Infantrymen equipped with items of clothing sufficient for indefinite protection at 0°C, with a natural wind velocity of 15 m.p.h., are to be transported in open lorries at 40 m.p.h. What is the effective change in insulation and period of cold tolerance due to the convection effect of high wind velocity?

(4) Two jungle uniforms are available. One is of material especially designed to resist insect bites, but this material is less porous and slightly heavier than the other. Will the heavier textile construction interfere with moisture transfer and cause a sensibly greater dehydration loss and circulatory stress, resulting in discard of the equipment by personnel?

Hundreds of questions similar to those given above, all of which directly involved an expert knowledge of the quantitative effect of clothing insulation on human temperature regulation, were presented to physiologists from equipment and medical divisions of all units of the armed forces. Detailed and quantitative answers were desired, and frequently the nature of this advice was a starting point in a long process of design, manufacture, and eventual global distribution of millions of items of clothing. In addition to field tests, laboratory methods for predicting the probable thermal value and climatic adaptability of dress assemblies were desperately needed. In answer to this need, methods of evaluation were developed which have resulted in valuable studies of clothing insulation in relation to varying conditions of human activity and exposure. The extent of this wartime literature and its highly specific nature preclude detailed review here. The basic methods of clothing analysis devised in the course of these investigations do, however, deserve description.[54]

The fundamental equations cited in Chapters II and III, or equivalent equational statements, are basic to any analysis of human heat loss. Their practical difficulties in application are two-fold. For extreme levels of activity or severe cold or heat exposure, the period required to reach a steady state of heat loss is prolonged. This is a result of the high heat capacity of the human body and of its relatively great thermal inertia. Furthermore, these periods of adjustment represent tolerance times, knowledge of which is often quite as important as a determination of the steady state.

Considerable progress in meeting these difficulties has been made by determining tolerance times empirically with representative subjects at a given exposure, and with a given protective clothing assembly. Such determinations have then been related to supplementary determinations, on electrically heated body models, of the steady state insulation of the clothing assembly. This steady state value may be rapidly attained by the use of heated metallic mannikins which reproduce in size and form the dimensions of an average human being. Heat is produced electrically in the body segments of such mannikins. By proper design this heat is distributed so that the different rates of heat loss from the torso, head, and extremities approximate those of the human subject under comfortable conditions. By variations of the total quantity of heat, the model may simulate a man at rest or working at various levels of increased heat production. Although wide use of such models had been made previously by A. C. Burton,[18] the Fatigue Laboratory, and the Pierce Laboratory in wartime research, the first technical description of a satisfactory model was published by Hall [45] in 1946.

The models have a low heat capacity and hence quickly reach a steady state. In addition, the heat input (simulated metabolism) can be more accurately determined than in the human subject. Furthermore, the complicating factor of evaporation may be eliminated from the determination of radiation-convection insulation value. Shulman[116] determined the insulation of a heavy Arctic assembly on human subjects and on a heated model, and found that the two methods gave values well within 5 per cent of the mean value.

Preliminary tests of clothing insulation value were often made with a simple blackened copper cylinder with spherical caps, maintained at a constant temperature, the measure of heat input necessary to maintain this temperature giving a measure of the heat loss from its surface when covered with the clothing material to be tested. This instrument had a base radius of 7.1 cm. with a vertical cylinder element height of 17.8 cm.

Influence of Clothing in Reducing Heat Loss by Convection in a Cold Environment

Ordinary experience encourages the belief that we can obtain practically any degree of insulation desired by adding successive layers of clothing materials. That this is not always the case is indicated by an experiment reported by Shulman. The test cylinder, in this case, was covered by one thickness of underwear fabric and over this were placed successive layers of Shelton double-pile fabric, a material with high insulation against convective heat loss. The conductance of the bare blackened cylinder was 6.36 kilogram-calories per square meter per hour per degree of temperature difference between its surface and that of the surrounding air, and this factor was reduced to 4.98 by the addition of one thickness of medium weight underwear fabric (0.2 to 0.3 cm. thickness). The reductions in the heat loss factor of 4.98, obtained by adding successive layers of double-pile fabric were as follows:

One layer of cloth was highly effective, two, three and four layers were better but were decreasingly effective. With five and six layers the heat loss was actually greater than with four layers. This seemingly paradoxical result, an increase in heat loss as the result of additional insulation, in small cylinder tests, has given rise to occasional statements to the effect that in adding clothing to a man for cold protection, there is an optimum thickness beyond which the additional protection afforded not only becomes negligible but even increases heat loss. The reason cited for this phenomenon is that additional layers of clothing increase the total surface from which the clothed body loses heat to its atmospheric environment. No one questions this statement in so far as it involves a systematic decrease in the overall insulation efficiency gained from successive insulating layers of equal thickness. We also know that there is a practical limit to clothing insulation determined by bulkiness, weight, and interference with the wearer's physical activity. However, the assumption that there is a reversal

Insulation	Heat loss in kg.-cal./m.²/°C difference, cyl. to air	Reduction in heat loss, per cent	Direction of insulation change	Spherical surface / Vertical surface
Blackened cylinder plus underwear	4.98			.75
Plus 1 layer of pile fabric	2.46	51	+	.80
Plus 2nd layer of pile fabric	1.48	70	+	.86
Plus 3rd layer of pile fabric	1.07	79	+	.92
Plus 4th layer of pile fabric	.69	86	+	.97
Plus 5th layer of pile fabric	.77	84	−	1.03
Plus 6th layer of pile fabric	.88	82	−	1.08

in the protective effect of insulation beyond a certain point leads to the first-order assumption that with sufficiently heavy clothing, an individual might be as poorly insulated as if he wore no clothing at all. This is, of course, not the case. Yet it is apparent that there is an optimum thickness beyond which one or two additional layers afford the wearer somewhat less insulative protection than with a lesser thickness of clothing. This effect has been seen in heated cylinder insulation tests, and it is conceivable that it occurs in the human body in locations which have a dimensional similarity to small test cylinders.

121

The explanation of this paradox, in so far as our clothing insulation tests with spherically capped heated cylinders are concerned, appears to depend on the combination of two shapes in such testing apparatus. In the preceding table the ratio of the spherical surface to the vertical cylinder wall surfaces has been given in the right hand column. It can be noted that as the bare spherically capped cylinder of 7.1 cm. radius increases in radius with clothing additions, there is a gradual increase in the percentage of spherical surface. Finally, with the addition of the fifth layer, the area of spherical surface exceeds the vertical cylindrical area. It may also be noted that at this point we first see evidence of a reversal of the increase in insulating value, with an actual increase in heat loss attributable to the addition of the fifth and sixth layers (r at sixth layer = 10.6 cm.).

If we take this changing ratio of spherical to vertical cylinder surface as a cue and investigate the relative heat loss of small spheres and cylinders, a very reasonable explanation is afforded for the phenomenon. Peclet[102] has shown that for spheres 5 to 30 cm. in diameter and cylinders 5–50 cm. in length the convective heat losses are respectively proportional to $(1.778 + (.13/r))$ and $(2.058 + (.038/r))$ where r is the radius in meters. In applying these formulas to the apparatus used in our tests, it can be shown that the spherical area contributed about 52 per cent of the convective heat loss in the bare cylinder of 7.1 cm. radius. When the test cylinder was increased to a radius of 10.6 cm. through the addition of 6 layers of pile fabric, the computation indicates that the spherical surface elements accounted for 70 per cent of the convective heat loss. Since for all values of r between 7.1 and 10.6 cm. the formulas above give substantially higher convective losses for the spherical elements, it is quite reasonable that we should find an increase in heat loss near the radius value at which the spherical surface first exceeds the cylinder surface. It is also quite obvious that at greater radius values (corresponding to further insulation) the overall insulative value will not continue to decrease, but will follow the usual relation of increase at a diminishing rate. Hence, our sudden apparent reversal in insulative value near the fifth layer of pile fabric, while real in a test sense, is seen to be a result of a test instrument involving two shape factors. Such shape factors do occur in the extremities of the heavily clothed human body. Although the above analysis has been made with respect to convection alone, the subsidiary place of radiation under the air movement of the test situation (30 to 40 feet per minute) and in practical cold exposure fully warrants this interpretation.

We have devoted considerable space to this discussion for several reasons.

In the first instance, it will emphasize the fact that in the range of radii (4 to 12 cm.) characteristic of at least 70 per cent of the body surface, the shape factor has a substantial influence on the rate at which overall insulation value changes with increasing thickness of protective clothing. In the second instance, it affords a reasonable explanation for the surprising statement often heard that under certain conditions additional clothing increases heat loss, and labels this statement as an observed phenomenon only in certain test situations without negating its possible importance in clothing insulation problems. However, the most substantial impression to be drawn from these data is the probable inaccuracy of any test situations for clothing insulation other than tests on normally dimensioned replicas of the human body or human subjects.

It is, in any case, abundantly clear that from a practical standpoint the provision of additional layers of clothing cannot add materially to thermal insulation beyond a certain point. In the use of either human subjects or large anatomical models for the evaluation of clothing insulation values, adaptations of the fundamental principles of partitional calorimetry discussed in Chapter III are necessary. Herrington[54] provides formulas by which the relationship between insulating value and surface area may be evaluated; but in order to apply them, the actual exposed surface of the clothed body must be computed, and no standard tables are available which supply such data. This problem has received considerable attention at our Laboratory. Sharply outlined silhouettes for the nude and the clothed subject are photographed with the subject in a lateral position, with the arms extended at the level of the shoulders. The areas of the resulting nude and clothed silhouettes are then determined by paper-weight methods or by the use of a planimeter. The surface area of the nude subject is separately estimated from the DuBois height-weight formula and compared with the silhouette area of the nude. The silhouette area is determined by applying a correction for photographic reduction and multiplying by the factor 5.02. This factor[10] relates the lateral silhouette area to the surface area of the body as a whole. The surface area of the clothed body may be estimated on the basis of the above relations and of the photographically determined ratio between the nude and clothed silhouettes.

In practical application this method will be found tedious and may involve an attempt at precision which is out of proportion to the accuracy required when variability in clothing fit and eccentricities of design are considered. Indeed, one may go further and note that with any clothing other than a skin-type vestment or an enveloping sack, it is very difficult to define the effective surface which is operative in thermal interchange. In the case of evaporative exchange, as an example, a textile surface of the same profile area as that of the human body may provide a surface much more effective in evaporation than a skin profile of equal area, since its actual fiber surface is very much larger than the profile area of the fabric.

These difficulties, however, do not obviate the need for the use of some reasonably consistent surface in the partition of heat loss from the clothed body. For this reason it appears necessary to define an effective clothing surface in some manner permitting direct and rapid approximation from easily determined measurements. We believe that such a "standard" clothing surface can be usefully estimated from the total weight of all clothing elements. In the table below, the relation between surface areas as determined by the silhouette method and the weight of clothing worn is given for total clothing weights varying from 0 to 10.5 kg. The lighter assembly, which includes shoes, socks, and light underwear, is typical of the cool weather protection worn at outdoor temperatures near 10°C with moderate activity. The heaviest assembly, weighing 10.5 kg., is composed of ordinary shoes, heavy woolen underwear, normal weight trousers and shirt, heavy woolen socks, high fur-lined boots, fur-lined leather jacket and outdoor trousers, fur-lined leather gloves, and sheepskin cap; in short, what might be worn for the most extreme exposure. Heavier dress than this is so cumbersome that we may reasonably conclude that this is a practical upper limit in protective clothing from the standpoint of weight and bulk.

It may be noted in the following table that the silhouette method for surface area agrees with the DuBois surface in the case of the nude, hence we may assume that the method yields a reasonable approximation for the dressed condition. On inspecting these values it can be seen that for relatively tight form-fitting clothing, the total area increases about one-tenth of a square meter for each kilogram of clothing (all items included).

Dress	Surface area, m.^{2} DuBois ht.-wt.	Silhouette method, m.^{2}	Weight of all clothing, kg.	Increase in surface area per kg. of clothing, m.^{2}
1. Nude	1.70	1.67	0	0
2. Pants, shirt, leather jerkin	—*	2.17	4.7	.10
3. Heavy cold weather clothing	—*	2.64	6.7	.15
4. Arctic equipment	—*	3.05	10.5	.13

* Formula not applicable to clothed figure.

125

For distinctly heavy clothing, where loosely fitted double pants and heavy fleece-lined jackets are used, this ratio is between 0.13 and 0.15. If we assume that the fit of normal dress approximates that of Condition 2, normal dress with a total weight of 3.5 kg. should give a clothing surface of 2.05 m.² for this subject if the factor of Condition 2 is applied. The mean increase in surface for all examples in the above table is 0.127 m.² per kg. of clothing. We believe that where the equations given on later pages are applied to the subject wearing clothing of the types ordinarily found to be efficient, the value of .13 m.² per kg. of clothing may be used to approximate the exposed area without important error. Direct determinations of this area are preferable, but in application to civil and industrial situations in which heat or cold stress calculations are applied to an average individual, this is usually not feasible. The average factor in the above table, 0.127 m.² per kg. of clothing, when applied to an individual of average stature, gives the following estimated clothing surface areas:

Dress	Area, m.²	Weight of clothing, kg.
1. Nude	1.80	0
2. Work pants, light underdrawers, shoes and socks	1.95	1.20
3. #2 plus light undershirt, and shirt	2.10	2.39
4. #3 plus vest, coat and tie	2.24	3.48

In this table the conditions of dress apply to heavy work under warm conditions (2), moderate work under warm conditions, or light work under hot conditions (3), and finally to all conditions under which standard conventional male attire is either usual or obligatory (4).

In general, adaptation to cold conditions can be effected—up to a certain point, as pointed out above—by increasing the thickness and weight of clothing above the normal value of (4) in the table above.

In using the weight as an approximate measure of thermal insulation, it is important to emphasize the assumption that the clothing used is of the type normally employed for thermal protection, that is, of a loosely woven and loosely fitting type. Actually this insulation value is primarily due, not to the characteristics of the clothing fabric itself, but to the provision within the fabric of air spaces in which air movement is almost nil. Wool is an excellent insulating fabric because the resilience of its fibers maintains the original volume of trapped air for a considerable period of time. Cotton is a relatively poor insulating material because of its lack of fiber resilience. In general, then, the insulating value of a clothing assembly depends on its thickness, irrespective of the material tested,[107] and on the looseness of its fit. A weighty assembly of skin-tight cotton duct would be very much less effective in insulation that a similar weight made up of several layers of loosely fitting wool. Clothing provides insulation primarily because it traps air and as a consequence insulation values tend to approximate the value for still air in a thickness comparable to the fabric.[118] In fact, the thermal insulation of an air space filled with steel wool packed to a density of 9 pounds per cubic foot, was found to be only 20 per cent less than the value for still air. With the types of cold-weather clothing actually in use, thickness and insulation value correspond closely to weight.

Many efforts were made during the war period to increase the insulation value of the usual fabrics. Such efforts introduced reflective layers for radiation insulation, tested the effect of various gases other than air in the fabric spaces, or attempted to delay cooling by the use of capacity effects, usually hydrated elements situated in the interior of the clothing. Probably none of these methods could be said to have achieved substantial gains, although flexible fabrics with aluminum

127

surfacing may yet prove to have an application in the clothing field. This situation may be modified in the future by the development of fabrics of fundamental low heat conductance or of fabrics in which air is contained within the fibers themselves. Tests made in our laboratory showed that an undergarment made of a plastic fiber with air bubbles inside it, when worn under a shirt and trousers by a copper dummy, showed 39 per cent more insulating value than an ordinary woolen undergarment. So far as materials now in general use are concerned, however, it would appear that the sheep has done a pretty good job of providing convection insulation.

One general conclusion that is clearly justified is that the attainment of adequate insulation against severe cold exposure is limited by the inability of conventional insulating fabrics to reduce heat transfer beyond a certain point without impossible increases in bulk. In addition, it must be realized that under extreme exposure the parallel paths of heat loss from the exposed skin, from the lungs, and through clothing ventilation seriously reduce the efficiency of any specific clothing insulation. It has also been found that the bulk factor is of special importance in limiting the effectiveness of insulation for the extremities. These three difficulties have led to the general use of electrical heating in aviation, and an emphasis on auxiliary heat for other severe exposures.

There is another factor which must be taken into account in estimating the insulating value of clothing, and that is the resistance of the exterior surface to the penetration of wind movement, which we have called the windbreak effect. Obviously, if a clothing assembly includes a non-porous layer and a layer containing insulating air, the non-porous material will be most effective on the outside. This is the reason for the use of leather outer garments. We can, perhaps, improve on the sheep by reversing the relative positions of skin and wool. In Figure 20 data obtained by the Climatic Research Laboratory* on this point have been reproduced. The insulation of

*Reproduced by permission of the Office of the Quartermaster General.

alpaca pile with pile in and out has been compared. At low outdoor air velocities of 100 to 200 feet per minute (about 1

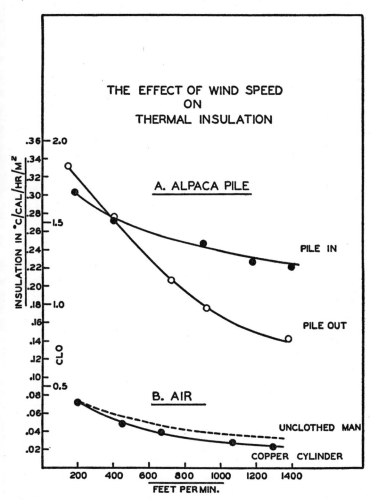

Figure 20. Effect of wind velocity on insulation value of clothing. (Reproduced from Climatic Research Laboratory Report 43, August 1943, by permission.)

to 2 m.p.h.), there is a small difference in favor of pile outside. At velocities over roughly 4 m.p.h., the pile-in has a noticeable superiority. The ordinate in Figure 20 is in terms of clo units, an insulation unit which will be discussed later in this chapter, and also in resistance units, the reciprocal of the overall insulation expressed as a conductance. A thermal resistance of .36°C/cal./hr./m.² means that the introduction of 1 kg.-cal. per hour per square meter in the test object, or its production by a human subject, will produce a temperature difference of 0.36°C between the object and the environment.

Finally, moisture effects may materially influence heat loss, particularly on sudden change from one environment to another. On passing from a low to a high humidity (at a given temperature), moisture is absorbed from the atmosphere to the clothing with liberation of heat. On passing from a moist to a dry environment, on the other hand, a temporary chilling effect is produced by evaporation. For example, on passing at 16°C, with a given clothing assembly, from a relative humidity of 30 per cent to one of 79 per cent, 30 calories were produced in one hour; in exchanging these same environments in the reverse direction, 20 calories were lost in the first hour.[92] The effect is especially serious, of course, when a person who has been exercising vigorously remains at rest in a dry atmosphere.

In Figure 21 the changes in moisture content of a woolen suit weighing 1.86 kg. when dry at 21°C have been illustrated for a variety of environmental changes in temperature and relative humidity. It can be easily seen from the weight changes involved (1 gm. change = 0.58 kg.-cal.) that heat gains and losses from clothing hydration may be of the order of one-third to one-half of the resting human heat production, and hence constitute an important element in heat exchange during movement between environments of different humidity. Relative humidity rather than temperature is the most important element in determining the moisture status of the fabric. Indirectly, of course, as in transitions from outdoors to indoors in winter, the temperature is primarily responsible for the relative humidity change.

Protective Effect of Decreasing Radiative Heat Loss

Since such materials as copper and aluminum are characterized by very low rates of emissivity to the surrounding radiation environment, the use of such materials on the outside of a clothing assembly naturally suggests itself

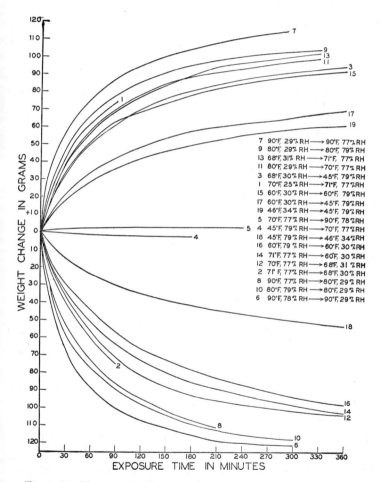

Figure 21. Hygroscopic effects on clothing weight of changing from a given atmosphere (left column of table) to one in which either temperature or relative humidity, or both, are different.

as a possibility. Experiments made on this point with a blackened cylinder (having very high emissivity) were moderately encouraging. This bare cylinder lost heat a a rate of 6.36 kg.-cal./m.²/hr./°C (temperature difference between the surface of the cylinder and the environment). The addition of one layer of underwear plus one layer of brown medium-weight woolen suiting gave a rate of heat loss of 3.98 (reduction of 39 per cent), while one layer of underwear plus one layer of copper cloth, plus one layer of aluminum cloth (with its metallic side outward) gave a rate of 2.52 (reduction of 60 per cent).[116] The clothing of troops in aluminum-surfaced fabrics would be highly undesirable from the standpoint of visibility; but in civilian life there seem to be distinct possibilities. Clothing of this kind would be especially helpful in aviation or mountain climbing, since, with increased rarefication of the air, convective heat loss decreases and the importance of radiative heat loss becomes relatively greater.

In outdoor environments where air movement is usually substantial, convective heat loss is quantitatively much more important than radiation loss, and this factor reduces the insulation advantage to be gained from an external reflective surface to a small value, at least in cold environments where heat conservation is desired and where gains from solar radiation would be desirable rather than otherwise. Radiation barriers situated internally in clothing may, however, have a useful function in providing insulation of reduced bulk.

Principles of Measuring Clothing Insulation and the "Clo" Unit

The methods of studying heat interchanges between the human body and its environment by the procedures of partitional calorimetry have been discussed in earlier chapters. The fundamental relationships involved, as we have pointed out earlier, may be expressed as follows:

(1) $\quad M \pm \Delta H - E = K_r (T_S - T_W) + K_C (T_S - T_A),$

where

$M =$ metabolism in kg.-cal./hr.,

$\Delta H =$ net heat change in total heat content of the body mass expressed in kg.-cal./hr. (When ΔH represents an increase in body temperature, its calorie value is subtracted from M; conversely, values representing decreases are added to M.),

$E =$ evaporative loss computed as .58 $\times$ the evaporative weight loss in grams/hour,

$K_R =$ constant of radiation exchange per °C difference between the average surface temperature of the body and that of the enclosing walls,

$T_S =$ average temperature of the body surfaces,

$T_W =$ average temperature of the wall surfaces,

$T_A =$ average temperature of the ambient air surrounding the body,

$K_C =$ constant of convection exchange per °C difference between T_S and T_A.

In the case of the clothed subject, this equation becomes

(2) $M \pm \Delta H - E = K_R (T_{cl} - T_W) + K_C (T_{cl} - T_A),$

where

$T_{cl} =$ average temperature in °C of the exposed skin *and* clothing surfaces of the body system.

133

The elements of equations (1) and (2) have been stated without introducing a specific area factor, and in this form they imply a heat balance for a human being of average area. In practice it is customary to express the terms $M + \Delta H - E$ in kg.-cal./m.^{2}, and likewise to use unit area values for the constants K_R and K_C. In this latter connection it must be observed that the value for K_C, the convection loss, is a function of air movement, and the area involved is that of the nude body, or the exposed skin plus the clothing surface. Also the radiation constant is not, strictly speaking, a constant, since the radiation exchange between two surfaces is not a linear function of their temperature difference, but is proportional to a fourth power difference. The area involved in radiation loss is somewhat less than the true surface area, and expressions in unit area should employ a radiation area equal to 75 per cent of the surface area. The effect of these modifications may be seen in equation (3), which is in a form permitting direct computation of heat loss, and recognizing the restrictions noted above. The radiation expression is not in an exact fourth-power-difference form, but is in a convenient form for calculation, and yields results of adequate accuracy.

$$(3) \quad M \pm \Delta H - E = .75 \times (4 \times 4.92 \times 10^{-8})$$
$$\times \frac{T_W^3 + (273° + T_{cl})^3}{2} + 1.0 \sqrt{V} \, (T_{cl} - T_A).$$

In this expression, the factor $+1.0 \sqrt{V}$ represents the convection loss per M^2 per hour per °C where V is the velocity of air movement in cm./sec., and replaces the expression $K_C(T_{cl} - T_A)$ in equation (2). The remaining terms define $K_R(T_{cl} - T_W)$ as given in (2). Where nude subjects are concerned, T_S may be substituted for T_{cl}. In application to the nude body the above relations will yield the total heat loss when multiplied by the surface area of a given subject. In application to the clothed body, the required total surface must be estimated. For any given atmospheric condition and subject activity, the physiological effect of a given clothing assembly and its physical insulation value may be determined from paired partitions using equations (2) and (3). In order to make equation (3) serviceable for practical calculations involving the clothed human body, some procedure for determining the surface of the clothed individual must be employed, such as has been described in an earlier paragraph.

The widespread use of partitional methods of estimating heat and cold stress from subjects and models created a need for a unit of heat insulation which would have practical meaning for non-technical groups. Such a unit should be convertible into the B.T.U./ft.^{2}/°F used by the ventilating engineer, the physicist's gram-cal./sec./°C, and the physiologist's kg.-cal./hr./°C, without being dependent upon these units for an approximate subjective appreciation of its insulation value. With these points in mind, Gagge, Burton, and Bazett[35] defined a practical unit, the "clo." One clo unit of thermal insulation is the clothing required to keep a resting subject in a comfortable state when the subject is seated in an atmosphere of 70°F, with relative humidity less than 50 per cent and air movement at 20 ft./min. (10 cm./sec.). The standard value for the metabolism associated with this condition is 50 kg.-cal./m.^{2}/hr. (one "met"). There is, of course, no cause and effect relation between the met and the clo. The two units merely represent multiples of average resting heat production and average comfortable clothing insulation.

The standardization of the clo unit utilized the experimental work of Winslow, Gagge, and Herrington[133] to determine that the total insulation which is the sum of the insulation of the clothing, I_{cl}, and that of the air, I_A, is

$$(4) \quad I_{cl} + I_A = \frac{33 - 21}{38} = 0.32 \frac{°C}{kg.\text{-}cal./hr./m.^2}.$$

The insulation of the air in metric units at the air movement cited is

(5) $$0.14 \frac{°C}{\text{kg.-cal./hr./m.}^2},$$

By difference the insulation of the clothing, equal in the above definition to 1 clo is

(6) $$0.32 - 0.14 = 0.18 \frac{°C}{\text{kg.-cal./hr./m.}^2},$$

or

$$0.88 \frac{°F}{\text{B.T.U./hr./ft.}^2}.$$

The clo definition is in terms of resistance rather than conductance units, since the former may be added directly to obtain the total resistance from known sub-components. The resistance[18] is given by the ratio of the driving force, here the temperature difference, to the flow per unit area of cross section, so that the

$$\frac{\text{Total Insulation}}{\text{(clothing plus air)}} = \frac{T_S - T_A \ (°C)}{\text{kg.-cal./m.}^2\text{/hr.}},$$

and a standard value for this relation is defined by equation (6). Perhaps something is added to the sensory appreciation of this unit by the following example. With low air movement and moderate humidity, the resting nude subject is comfortable at 30°C (86°F). One clo of insulation is required to maintain the same degree of comfort when the air temperature is dropped to 21.2°C (70°F). Extending this analogy, one may say that two clo is the clothing sufficient for comfort at 12.4°C (54°F), three clo that sufficient for 3.6°C (38°F), and so on, each additional clo permitting a drop of about 8.8°C (16°F) from the nude comfort level at air temperature 30°C (86°F), it being understood that air movement and heat production remain in agreement with the formal definition.

It is probably obvious that one clo is very nearly the insulation provided by normal male clothing. This is intentional, and provides a valuable experience correlation for the unit. The clo unit is by definition an arbitrary unit. It is of some interest to note that modern science is not alone in having coined an insulation unit for clothing in which objective and subjective factors are correlated. We are told that Chinese peasants index the weather in terms of "suits." Warm and comfortable weather being referred to as a "one-suit day," and increasing degrees of cold being termed "two suit," "three suit" on up to a limit of "twelve suits," indicating severe weather.

Elapsed time	T_A	T_S	T_R	T_{Cl}	M*	E	ΔH	I_A	I_{Cl}	Clo units
Minutes	°C	°C	°C	°C	kg.-cal./m.²/hr.					
0	—	—	—	—	—	—	—	—	—	—
40	16.2	33.18	37.04	26.0	53.0	10.3	11.4	.18	.13	.72
80	16.2	32.75	36.97	25.8	50.5	10.3	11.1	.19	.13	.72
120	16.1	32.36	36.89	25.6	50.2	10.3	9.7	.19	.14	.78
160	16.2	31.87	36.82	25.1	51.4	10.3	12.4	.17	.13	.72
200	16.1	31.60	36.76	25.0	53.3	10.3	7.7	.18	.13	.72

* M = Metabolism. E = evaporation. ΔH = Heat Change of the net change in body temperature. I_A and I_{Cl} are insulation values of air and clothing, respectively, in $\dfrac{°C}{kg.\text{-}cal./m.²/hr.}$. T_R = rectal temperature.

In the table above, data on the time course of the heat adjustment of a normally clothed male subject are given.[133] This table illustrates the elements necessaray for a calculation of the basic insulation of the air and of the clothing in the usual metric units. In the extreme right hand column the clothing insulation has been converted into clo units to illustrate the above discussion. It should be noted that the insulation factor of air, I_A, and of clothing, I_{Cl}, yield relatively constant values despite the absence of a complete steady state. This is made possible by computing the factor, ΔH, representing changes in average body temperature and applying it to the equation

$$M \pm \Delta H - E = R + C$$

where

$$R + C = \text{net heat loss.}$$

In computing ΔH, the changes in skin temperature receive a weight of 1, the changes in rectal temperature a weight of 2. Since the body is cooling, this average temperature change multiplied by the specific heat of the body, .83, and the weight of the subject, yield a result in kg.-cal./hr., which is divided by the surface area and added to M, the measured heat production. E, the evaporation loss, is subtracted.

In the table above, the insulation value of the air, I_4, is greater than the value on which the clo unit was standardized, reflecting the difference between air movement of 4.6 cm./sec. and 10 cm./sec. Such values for the insulation of the "air" include both radiation and convection effects from the surrounding environment. In order to separate these effects for unusual radiation exposures and air movement, equation (3) must be applied, utilizing measurements of radiant temperature and of air movement.

Although it is usual to consider the clothing as a unit of thermal resistance interposed between the body and the environment, this is not strictly true. At very low temperatures, or with high wind velocities, considerable quantities of heat flow along parallel paths of heat loss, and do not pass through the clothing proper. Heat loss by respiration, direct losses from exposed skin, and both evaporative and convection losses due to ventilation of the clothing fall into this category.

In the table above, a calculation of the amount of heat which "short-circuits" the clothing barrier has been made. It can be seen that even at 0°C the processes of respiration and insensible evaporation may account for as much as one-third of the resting heat loss. To this may properly be added a less certain increment due to clothing ventilation and loss from the exposed facial skin which may raise the total short-circuit

138

Estimated parallel heat losses: Respiration
Clothing ventilation
Skin evaporation
$R + C$ from exposed face

1	2	3	4	5	6	Respiration rate (900 liters/min)
Temp.	Respired* heat loss at sea level	Skin E	Clothing ventilation	Face loss†		Total of 2, 3, and 6
				T_S	kg.-cal. °C	
°C	kg.-cal./hr.	kg.-cal./hr.	kg.-cal./hr.			
15	16.6	9.0	Unknown	25.5	12.6	38
0	23.8	9.0	"	18.0	21.6	54
− 5	25.7	9.0	"	15.5	24.6	59
−15	28.9	9.0	"	10.5	30.6	69
−25	31.6	9.0	"	5.5	36.6	77
−35	33.8	9.0	"	−0.5	42.6	85
−45	36.8	9.0	"	−4.5	48.6	95

* Inspired air saturated at air temperatures; expired air saturated at 33°C. Sum of sensible and insensible losses. Kg.-cal. per hour per 900 liters per minute respiration rate.

† Face loss has been estimated by assuming that 4 per cent of the body area is facial and exposed directly, that the T_S of this exposed area is the mean of exposure air and 36°C. The latter gives facial skin temperatures of the order of 0°C at −35° and −45°C, a point recognized as one at which the exposed portions of the face are likely to freeze at even normal air movements. As a local radiation-convection constant, a value of 1.2 kg.-cal./hr./0.07 m.² (4 per cent of the total) per °C difference between T_A and T_S has been used.

of the clothing barrier to one-half of the resting heat loss. Emphasis has been given to this illustration because it is a factor of great importance at low temperatures, and is perhaps the principal difficulty in the direct application of the clo value of an assembly to unusual conditions. This difficulty is, in brief, the fact that we have a series resistance in the clothing, and, in addition, parallel paths of heat loss related to exposed skin, respiration, and garment ventilation.

If these limitations are borne in mind, reasonably acceptable predictions of the performance and protective value of clothing may be made from direct observations on human subjects. A formula which has been widely used for this purpose utilizes the definition of the clo unit by Gagge, Burton, and Bazett,[35] based on the experimental work of Winslow, Gagge, and Herrington.[134] A convenient form for computation has been given by Belding, Darling, Griffin, Robinson, and Turrell.[6] The insulation of air in clo units at different velocities required in this formula may be obtained from the work of Burton.[17] The formula is:

$$I_{Cl} = \frac{5.55\,(T_S - T_A)\,A}{M - .58E + 0.83w\,\dfrac{(2\Delta T_R + \Delta T_S)}{3}} - I_a,$$

where

I_{Cl} = over-all insulation of assembly in clo units,
I_A = insulation of air in clo units,
T_S = mean skin temperature, excluding temperature of hands, head and feet, $°C$,
T_A = ambient air temperature, $°C$,
A = body surface area (DuBois), m.^{2},
M = total metabolic rate determined from oxygen consumption, kg.-cal./hr.,
E = evaporation loss estimated from successive weighings of clothed subjects, loss in gms. $\times$ .58 = kg.-cal./hr.,
w = weight of unclothed subject, kg.,
0.83 = composite specific heat of human body, kg.-cal./kg./$°C$,
ΔT_R = rate of fall of rectal temperature, $°C$/hr.,
ΔT_S = rate of fall of mean skin temperature, $°C$/hr.,
5.55 = the reciprocal of the clo value, converts the total resistance, kg.-cal./m.^{2}/hr./$°C$ into clo units. Tests are carried out at a moderately low temperature with subjects at rest. Observations of T_S, M, E, T_R, and T_A are made between the second and third hour of exposure after the subject attain a steady cooling rate.

Experimental success in the application of this method of clo determination depends principally on reliable determinations of the various temperatures involved. Metabolic rate and evaporative loss may be determined by conventional methods with no difficulty. The application of thermocouples to the skin and clothing in a manner which will yield reproducible temperature results despite exercise is not as simple, and various laboratories have developed individual techniques. In our work, we have sampled skin and clothing areas at 15 points each, these points being so located as to yield fair samples of the segmental body surface areas represented in the standard DeBois measurement which allocates 7, 21, 31, and 41 per cent of the average nude surface area to the head, upper extremities, trunk, and lower extremities, respectively. In Figure

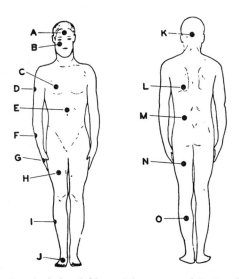

Figure 22. Standard skin fields used for mean and DuBois body segment skin temperature samples. Head: A,B,K; upper extremities: D,F,G; trunk: C,E,L,M; lower extremities: H,I,J,N.

22 these skin fields have been located on an anatomical figure.[137] In Plate I the multiple thermacouple unit attached to the skin is shown. Head temperatures were sampled by a ther-

mocouple not attached to the subject. The couples are arranged to average segmentally with the exception of toe and finger couples which are individual. All are recorded by a chart type recording potentiometer. The thermocouples are of a flexible type and the measuring junctions are centered in solder-filled 1-cm. copper discs so arranged as to seat on the skin through light elastic tension with adjacent skin areas free of harness contact. The reverse side of these button contactors may be seen in Plate I on the diagonal strap across the chest, just over the biceps, and midway in the thigh strap.

A somewhat different type of couple application has been found satisfactory for clothing surface temperature, and an acceptable method is illustrated in Plate II. This is the same subject after the application of 6 layers of clothing, and in these experiments each clothing layer as well as the skin surface was represented by an individual set of thermocouples, a total of over sixty temperature samples in the gradient between body surface and clothing surface. On all clothing surfaces it was found that more satisfactory temperature measurements resulted if the couple was attached to a sheet of copper foil 20×5 cm. Fabrics are poor conductors and a single point on a fabric surface is much less representative than a similar small point sample from a true skin surface. The light copper foil through its high heat conductivity averages the temperature laterally over an area of 100 cm.^{2} for each couple. Measurements made under these conditions are consistent and reproducible in repeated exposures. As a final detail it may be noted that in Plate II the final leads for each set of segmentally averaging thermocouples are brought to a junction strip on the subject's left arm at which point connection may be conveniently made to an automatic temperature recorder.

In all determinations of insulation value it is important to remember that the values derived are average insulation values. Heat loss is not uniform over the surface of the clothed body, and requirements of dress make large differences in local insulation value necessary. The hands, as an example, cannot be efficiently used if provided with a local insulation value equal to the average clo required for extreme conditions. Insulation of the hands to this extent would lead to gloves of ridiculous proportions. This problem of the insulation of the extremities will be discussed in a succeeding paragraph.

How the results of tests made on a copper dummy using these formulae worked out may be illustrated by comparison of two experiments reported by Shulman[116] and summarized in the table below. The two clothing assemblies tested were as follows:

Assembly A: "Standard" woolen underwear and a garment of ¼-inch Shelton brown double-pile material, with shearling head covering and gloves, socks, and shoes.

Assembly B: Heavy woolen underwear, and five clothing layers as follows:
Aluminum cloth with reflective side out, ⅜-inch double-pile,
Double layer of aluminum cloth with non-reflective sides facing each other, ⅜-inch double-pile,
Inverted sac of aluminum cloth, reflective side out, reaching to the ankles.

In addition, the mannikin wore woolen socks, two pairs of fleece-lined rubber boots, two pairs of gloves, a fleece-lined helmet, shearling over the face, and a silk scarf.

Two tests were made with Assembly B, one under normal atmosphere and the other in a decompression chamber.

Assembly	Corresponding altitude	$T_A{}^1$ °C	$T_S{}^2$ °C	$R + C^3$	K^4	Clo value
A	0	17.8	30.6	38.02	2.97	1.17
B	0	−20.0	9.8	35.32	1.19	3.97
B	26,000	−19.8	15.2	35.32	1.01	4.80

Thus, Assembly A, which corresponds to a normal winter costume (without an overcoat) has an insulating value of 1.17 clo, while the highly elaborate Arctic equipment of Assembly B raised the value to 3.97 clo. With its extensive radiative protection, the figure rose to 4.80 clo in an atmosphere corresponding to an altitude of 26,000 feet.

The comparison of clo values determined on subjects equipped as in Plates I and II, and of similar equipment on electrically heated anatomical models, provides a very desirable check, and since the model tests are free of evaporative complications, the model results are frequently of substantial help in determining the more complex thermal behavior of the fully clothed human subject. In our investigations several anatomical models were used. The most satisfactory of these is shown in Plate III. This model is of normal dimensions for a surface area of 1.8 m.² and was constructed by molding 1/32-inch copper sheeting over a papier mache form.* Access to the interior of the model is provided by a hinged plate 10 × 10 inches dorsally placed. Screw plates 1½ inches in diameter were placed at the vertex, in each palm, and on the upper surface of the feet. Heat is provided through 16 small variable wattage light bulbs enclosed in copper mesh cages and segmentally located so that the temperature topography of the model is similar to that of the comfortably cool person when nude and at rest in a room at 30°C with low air movement (see references in Chapter III). An internal connection box is located near the dorsal plate and plug-in outlets for a fan and heat control placed in the eye sockets. In order to simulate the metabolism of rest or different grades of work, the heat input is variable from 1 to 4 times the met unit (associated with the clo unit, see p. 135), or, in conventional terms, from about 1 to 5 times the basal metabolism.

In order more nearly to simulate the conditions of skin conductance, the finished copper mannikin was coated with

---

* Mr. C. W. Colby, of the Bridgeport Brass Company, constructed this model from specifications supplied by one of the authors.

an ⅛-inch layer of synthetic rubber dispersed in ethylene di-chloride. In this skin layer the measuring couples for seg-mental temperature have been located. The completed ap-paratus is an exceptionally useful tool for any laboratory con-cerned with human heat exchange in relation to climate and clothing. In Plate IV the partitional calorimeter is shown in which these models have been calibrated, and where a major portion of the problems on human heat exchange discussed in this book have been studied.

Physiological Alterations of the Thermal Properties of the Human Body in Relation to Clothing

In our discussion so far, heat loss analysis and tolerance data have been discussed without emphasis on the character of the body's temperature regulation activities. Vasomotor action, however, may definitely alter the conditions of heat loss in a manner strikingly similar to that produced by clothing. This reaction warrants discussion since it eventually has to be in-cluded in any complete analysis of heat loss from the clothed body.

Vasomotor effects on the heat conductance of the skin are somewhat analogous to the addition or removal of clothing from the nude body. The skin of the human body is richly sup-plied with blood vessels. Under cold stimulation the flow of blood through these vascular networks is greatly reduced. When exposed to heat, the flow near the skin surface is greatly increased. The net result of the former process is that the heat loss through the cold skin has to pass an insulation barrier which exceeds the resistance of the warm dilated skin by an amount equivalent to the insulating value of 1 to 1.5 cm. of fatty tissue. In computing the total resistance to heat loss from the deep regions of the body to air, this element of resistance due to vasomotor action is considerable. Burton[18] gives the following values in clo units for the practical range in variation of the resistance due to vasomotor action, clothing, and air.

Resistance element	Range in clo units	Cause of variation
Peripheral tissues	0.15–0.80	Vasomotor action
Clothing	1–4 clo	Choice of clothing
Air	0.2–0.8	Air movement

Analysis of thermal stress must be made both for resting and active occupations; hence it is of considerable importance to know whether or not the range in the resistance of the skin is different under the two circumstances. In the table below, data on the exercising subject obtained by Nielsen[97] have been re-computed to obtain values for the thermal conductance of the skin of a subject exercising on a bicycle ergometer at air temperatures between 9.3° and 36°C. Under the coolest condition, the low conductance of 14.4 kg.-cal./m.²/hr. is realized, and this value lies in a portion of the conductance curve which is asymptotic to air temperature. Hence we may assume that maximum vaso-constriction had been realized at this condition.

T_A °C	T_R °C	T_S °C	$M^* - W$	$T_R - T_S$ °C	$\dfrac{M - W}{T_R - T_S}$ (per 1.80 m.²)	K
9.3	38.3	21.0	467	17.3	27.0	14.4
15.0	38.3	23.7	467	14.6	32.0	17.0
19.6	38.3	26.7	467	11.6	40.3	21.4
29.0	38.3	32.0	467	6.3	74.1	39.4
36.0	38.3	35.3	467	3.0	155.7	82.8

* Metabolism in kg.-cal./hr./man. K = conductance, kg.-cal./hr./m.² (sometimes given per man instead of per m.²). W = the fraction of the energy metabolism dissipated as work on the environment (ergometer propulsion) rather than as bodily heat.

A similar study of resting subjects by Gagge, Winslow, and Herrington[38] gave a constricted value of 12 for conductance.

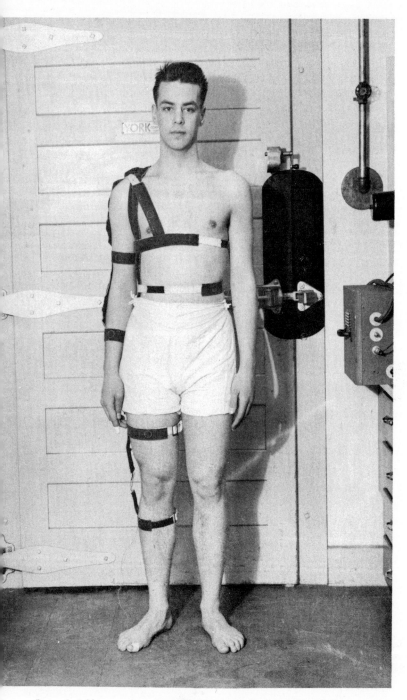

PLATE I. Subject wearing segmental skin temperature sampling harness.

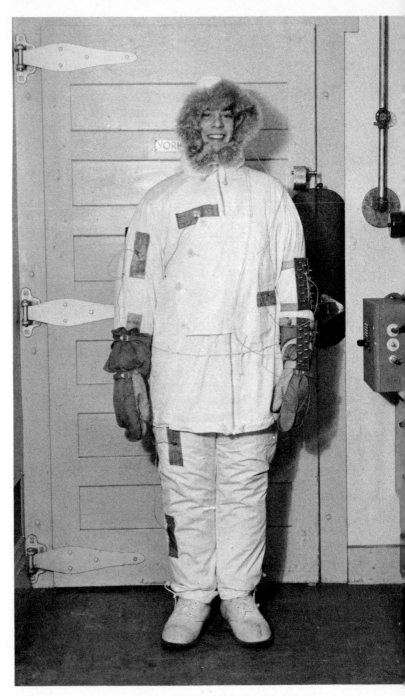

PLATE II. Illustration of the application of clothing
surface thermocouples and connection strips.

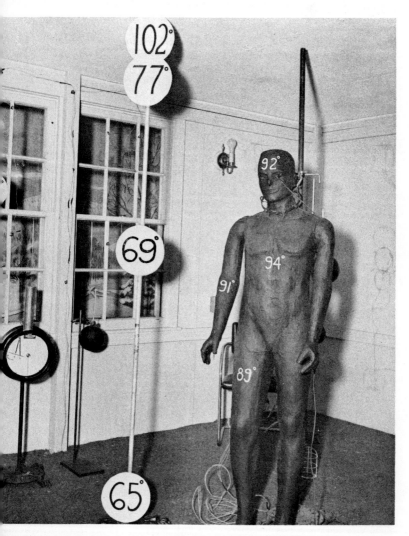

PLATE III. Electrically heated copper manikin of 1.8 square meters with variable heat input (to 5 times basal metabolism), and segmental control of surface temperature as used in determining insulation value of clothing items. Temperatures on the model represent average segmental skin temperatures of a normal clothed subject in a room with electrically heated ceiling (102°F) and air temperatures of 65°, 69°, and 77°F at the levels indicated.

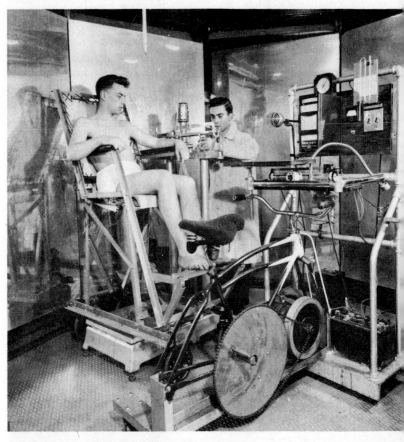

PLATE IV. Partitional calorimeter designed for the experimental separation of radiation, convection, and evaporative fractions of human heat loss, at rest and during exercise, over temperature range extending from sub-zero to tropical conditions. Biophysical and physiological data from such experiments form the background for thermal stress determination using models similar to the one shown in Plate III.

If we express the constricted and dilated conductance values for the exercising and resting subjects as resistances, we have the following relations:

Resting $\begin{cases} .026 \text{ dilated} \\ .083 \text{ constricted} \end{cases}$ Exercising $\begin{cases} .012 \text{ dilated} \\ .069 \text{ constricted} \end{cases}$

In both instances the absolute change in the thermal resistance of the skin, produced by vasodilation to heat is .057 kg.-cal./m.²/hr.; that is, exercise does not alter the thermal resistance decrease by vasodilation. Since different subjects were used in these two experiments, and since the skin temperature data of the two experiments were only approximately comparable, we can attach no importance to the exactness of the above agreement. We are quite justified in assuming, however, that there is no considerable variation in the thermal effect of dilation at rest and in exercise insofar as resistance is concerned.

If we use Lefevre's value of 23.8 kg.-cal./m.²-hr.-°C/cm. for the specific conductivity of tissue,[71] we obtain a ratio of: .057/.047 between the total resistance change due to vasomotor action and the specific thermal conductivity of tissue. This calculation indicates that in exercising or resting subjects, dilation is equivalent to the removal of a thermal resistance equivalent to 1.35 cm. of tissue. Quite obviously this is a considerable item in computing the sum of resistances, including clothing, which may lie between the deep body regions and the air.

In Figure 23 five illustrative pictograms and graphs have been redrawn from an article by A. C. Burton[18] on clothing in relation to heat exchange. Presentation of this type has been useful in demonstrating to laymen the practical significance of the clo unit of clothing insulation in relation to the met unit of human heat production under varied climatic exposures. In the pictograms labeled 1, 3, and 6 met, the position of the mercury at $+70°$, $+40°$, and $-5°$F illustrates the approxi-

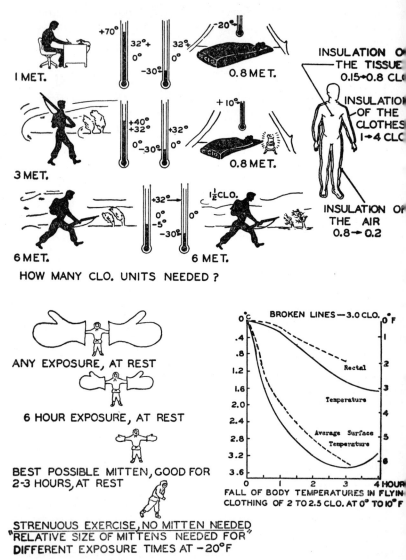

Figure 23. Graphic illustration of the interdependence of level of heat production, grade of insulation, and severity of exposure on the adequacy of protective clothing. See text for detailed explanation. (Redrawn from A. C. Burton, *Clothing and Heat Exchange.*)

mate decrease in environmental temperature which may be tolerated with standard clothing as heat production is increased from a sedentary level of 1 met (50 cal./m.^{2}/hr.) to 6 met representing severe exertion. The fourth exercising figure indicates that an increase of clothing insulation to 1½ clo with a heat production of 6 met permits a further drop in environmental temperature to −30°F. The two sleeping bag pictograms illustrate the choice that may be made between heavy or medium protection in sleeping bags (11 or 8 clo insulation value) provided auxiliary heating (stove) is used to raise a shelter temperature of −20°F to +10°F. In the outlined figure of a clothed man, a graphic indication has been given of the three components into which the total insulation of the clothed man has been analyzed by Burton.[18]

The mitten illustration emphasizes the difficulties which are met in trying to provide adequate insulation for the hands at an environmental temperature of −20°F. With this exposure, at rest, the amount of insulation required by the hand is greatly in excess of what is practically possible if the hand is to remain functionally useful. If the time of exposure is limited to two to three hours, protection may be provided with gloves whose bulk is within practical limits. Finally, if exercise is strenuous, the glove may be dispensed with. In such instances, the development of methods of measuring tolerance time when insulation is insufficient for continuous exposure have been of great utility. The mitten illustration was reproduced by Burton from studies on tolerance time made by Dr. John Talbot and the Climatic Laboratory of the Office of the Quartermaster General.

The graph reproduced in the lower right hand portion of Figure 23 was also obtained in studies at the Army Climatic Laboratory. This graph illustrates the average fall in rectal and skin temperature observed in 50 subjects seated in a cold chamber and clothed in heavy aviators' clothing. The changes observed are far larger than those which had been previously

149

observed in lightly clothed men subjected to a cooling stress. Apparently under heavily clothed conditions the deep body temperature falls to a much lower level before the protective responses of shivering (increased heat production) and vasoconstriction occur. Such delay in protective response is not observed, however, if the face is exposed to the stimulation of cold wind. It may be assumed that certain areas of the body which are normally exposed to cooling stress act as trigger areas in the stimulation of protective physiological processes, and if these areas are relatively well protected in the initial stages of the exposure, the response is delayed. In a practical sense this suggests that the complete enclosure of a sack-like garment may be less advantageous than clothing of approximately equal overall insulation value which permits limited exposure of certain skin areas.

In the correlation of clothing insulation studies with practical climatic problems an accurate interpretation of geographical and climatic data in relation to indices of clothing insulation and subsidiary data relative to climate quality and seasonal range is of the greatest importance. The movement to develop world-wide climatic maps indexed in terms of climatic stress and physiologically assessed clothing requirements is in large measure traceable to the persistent attention to this problem by Dr. Paul Siple, veteran Antarctic explorer, geographer, and climatologist. The wind chill index developed by Dr. Siple during exposure studies made in the Antarctic prior to 1940 was one of the first efforts to bring about a correlation between physiological investigations of human heat exchange and the physical properties of climate as experienced in the field. During the recent war Dr. Siple, working in contact with many civilian laboratories as well as service research stations, greatly advanced the development of the new field of climatic stress mapping, which has been, perhaps, the most valuable scientific advance in environmental physiology attained by studies of the type reviewed in this chapter.

150

Protection of the Extremities Against Extreme Cold

Since the hands and feet have a surface area which is very large in relation to their volume, and since they are serviced by blood vessels at the extreme periphery of the vasomotor system, it is in these extremities that the results of chilling are most acute. After exposure to cold, with its consequent vaso-constriction, a second and opposite adaptive process of vaso-dilation occurs in the extremities, which tends to protect them from painful local chilling. Even in an environment at 15°C, successive cycles of vasoconstriction and vasodilation have been observed. Local pain, chilblains, trench foot, and frost-bite are associated with such excessive cooling, and under con-ditions of continued exposure to wet cold, difficulties appear at temperatures substantially above freezing.

Special protection of the extremities against cold is there-fore indicated, in addition to such clothing as will maintain the general body temperature at a reasonable level. A few ex-periments made during the war have suggested that this is a promising field for research. In our laboratory a special glove was prepared with an internal vacuum space to provide con-vection insulation, and two layers of aluminum foil to furnish radiative insulation. This glove and an ordinary leather wool-lined flying glove were placed over rubber gloves filled with water just below boiling point, and the respective cooling curves were observed in an atmosphere of 16°C for 9 hours. The temperature of the water inside the special glove fell to 32°C in 5 hours as compared with less than 2 hours for the ordinary glove. After 9 hours, the temperature inside the special glove was 25.2°, while that inside the ordinary glove was 15.9°C.[116] Artificial heat obtained from chemical pads provides a partial solution of this problem, but it is conceivable that for certain situations pockets lined with a plastic vacuum element may prove useful.

Physiological Cost of Excess Clothing Under Hot Conditions

The principal advantageous effects of clothing under warm conditions are a possible reduction of solar heat gain and an increase in evaporative efficiency under certain circumstances. Its disadvantages are an increase in circulatory stress and dehydration effects where more clothing is required than is desirable from a purely thermal standpoint. In the table below, the variable dehydration stress that may be imposed by clothing is illustrated. These results show the sweat secretion of a young male subject working on a bicycle ergometer with a total heat production of 279 kg.-cal. per hour. This work is approximately equal to walking at 3 miles per hour with a 20-pound pack.

Dress	Sweat secretion in gms. per hour	
	at 85°F (29.4°C) 85% R.H.	at 110°F (43.3°C) 15% R.H.
	equivalent air movement 100 ft./min.	
Light underwear, shorts, moderate weight pants and shirt, shoes, light socks	470	700
Stripped to the waist	438	603
Shorts, underwear, socks, shoes	333	638
Athletic supporter, shoes and socks	260	652

These data show that at air temperatures above body temperature, with low humidity, the effect of clothing variation is not conspicuous at low air velocities. However, at moderately hot temperature with high humidity, the dehydration effect of added clothing is conspicuous. The thermal analysis of this differential effect is complicated, but in general the difference depends upon the importance of radiation and convection cooling at the 29.4°C condition, and the dominance of evaporative cooling at the 43.3°C condition. In the former case, the added clothing imposes an added heat load, while in the latter, no cooling is occurring by radiation and convection, and clothing affords an evaporative surface or wick action which is favorable. We have found in this laboratory[143] that with low relative humidity the clothed subject can adapt better than the nude subject up to 52°C, while with high relative humidity the reverse is the case. This explains in part why the dwellers in hot desert regions commonly wear reasonably heavy clothing, while those in hot humid climates go as nearly naked as possible.

In the majority of cases, however, the problems of hygiene of clothing at high temperatures are best evaluated by direct determination, as in the table above, of the dehydration cost of various assemblies, in relation to the increments in body temperature associated with this loss. There is at present no general agreement as to the absolute elevation of body temperature or rate of dehydration which is permissible for various types of work. Any given stress determined experimentally may, however, be profitably compared with the approximate limits determined by Robinson, Turrell, and Gerking[110] for steady state exposures, or the tolerance time index of Taylor.[121] Both of these reports deal with the grading of thermal stress in terms of measures of equivalent physiological response involving pulse accelerations, rate of dehydration, and body temperature increment.

The real hazards of heat stress are dehydration and circulatory exhaustion. Many industrial exposures unquestionably stress both functions to an unnecessary degree, even though the exposure is tolerated. Data which illustrate very clearly the added cardiac load and increased dehydration stress produced by hot environments have been reported by Robinson.[109] Since these data provide for two subjects of apparently different degrees of adjustive ability, a primary picture of the differential stress over a wide range of environmental conditions, they are of particular value. In Table A Robinson's data for these two subjects at rest have been reproduced. In Table B similar data are given for the same two subjects while walking.

These tables illustrate a very common problem in any attempt to define tolerance, namely, the extraordinary individual differences, related to training, acclimatization, age, and general fitness. Subject AJ in these experiments, is able to exercise at 45°C with a heart rate which is in the seventies, except for the condition at 42 per cent relative humidity, and

TABLE A*

Clothing: Shorts
Wind velocity (in room)
   2 m.p.h.

Average metabolism:
   46 kg.-cal./m.^{2}/hr.

Room temp. °C	Air humidity %	Subject	Conductance kg.-cal./ m.^{2}/hr.	Heart rate	Rectal temp. °C	Sweat g./hr.	Skin temp. °C
22.2	26	MS	6.0	76	37.1	44	32.4
21.8	31	AJ	5.1	50	36.2	42	30.8
28.1	25	MS	7.6	69	37.2	112	33.5
28.4	30	AJ	7.5	57	36.6	67	32.9
37.8	22	AJ	9.4	65	37.2	341	34.2
37.7	41	AJ	9.3	64	37.2	318	34.2
38.1	60	MS	12.5	82	37.4	395	35.2
38.1	60	AJ	13.9	60	37.2	301	35.2
37.8	76	AJ	15.6	69	37.5	719	35.7
44.7	41	MS	12.8	93	38.1	640	35.9
44.7	41	AJ	10.4	65	37.6	775	34.9
45.0	59	MS	—	105	38.5	1262	37.9
45.0	59	AJ	—	83	38.3	1529	38.1
45.1	11	AJ	11.9	65	37.4	623	35.1
50.2	44	MS	20.0	121	38.7	1372	38.3
50.2	44	AJ	16.7	86	38.0	1871	38.6
50.1	21	MS	—	90	37.7	825	36.3
50.1	21	AJ	—	60	37.6	817	35.9

* Data from o.s.r.d. Report by Dr. Sid Robinson, Number 12, May 14, 1944.

his general circulatory efficiency is such that rectal temperature is only a few tenths above its value for comparable exercise at 22.2°C. Despite these difficulties in the matter of individual tolerance, an inspection of the progressive increases in heart rate and sweat secretion as the exposure varies from 21.1° to 50°C affords a convincing picture of the heavy phys-

TABLE B*

Clothing: Shorts
Wind velocity (by man walking) 2.8 m.p.h.

Average metabolism: 130 kg.-cal./m.²/hr.

Room temp. °C	Air humidity %	Subject	Conductance kg.-cal./ m.²/hr.	Heart rate	Rectal temp. °C	Sweat g./hr.	Skin temp. °C
20.6	33	MS	11.6	93	37.5	103	31.5
20.6	33	AJ	9.9	72	37.4	100	30.5
21.8	31	MS	13.0	94	37.6	105	32.5
22.2	28	AJ	13.9	69	37.5	100	32.5
28.4	30	MS	18.1	93	37.6	279	33.8
28.1	25	AJ	18.4	69	37.3	255	33.5
28.4	80	MS	19.2	100	37.7	240	34.1
28.3	83	AJ	16.0	70	37.6	223	33.2
37.8	24	MS	28.4	93	37.6	624	35.1
37.8	18	AJ	22.3	73	37.6	604	34.5
37.8	41	MS	26.6	101	37.7	590	35.1
37.8	41	AJ	19.2	64	37.3	635	33.7
37.9	62	MS	30.5	99	37.7	679	35.4
37.9	62	AJ	29.8	64	37.5	870	35.2
37.9	76	MS	34.7	117	38.3	1160	36.3
37.9	75	AJ	37.9	89	38.2	1600	36.4
45.4	22	MS	33.8	105	37.9	876	35.9
45.4	15	AJ	20.2	77	37.7	909	34.2
45.4	23	AJ	21.2	74	37.7	966	34.4
45.3	41	MS	46.3	116	38.1	1020	36.6
45.3	42	AJ	40.3	92	38.0	1533	36.3
49.1	31	MS	43.1	114	38.2	1313	36.6
49.1	31	AJ	37.9	85	38.1	1618	36.2

* Data from o.s.r.d. Report by Dr. Sid Robinson, Number 12, May 14, 1944.

iological stress of increasingly hot environments. The eventual standardization of data of this type will, at some future date, provide a solid basis for the exact assessment of the physiological costs of many industrial activities which are, at present, discussed principally in terms of supposed "upper limits of tolerance."

Protection of the Head Against Solar Radiation

The influence of solar radiation upon the head, in dry and hot climates, has been the subject of much unscientific traditional interpretations. The old phrase, "mad dogs and Englishmen go out in the mid-day sun," has produced an exaggerated emphasis (particularly among Englishmen in the tropics) on the assumed harmful effects of sun on the head. Actually, we do not know certainly whether "sun-stroke" is specifically different from any other kind of "heat-stroke." Blum[12] has computed an approximate heat balance for a man marching at 3 miles per hour in dry desert air at 37°C with terrain at 60°C. This latter item is important in desert conditions since the solar heat load is composed of a reflected solar radiation from the ground, as well as direct solar radiation and sky radiation. He assigns the following tentative values to the elements of the heat exchange:

	kg.-cal./hr.
Metabolism	+265
Total solar heat load	+234
"Black body" radiation exchange with terrain	+128
"Black body" radiation exchange with sky	128
Evaporation	−506

If the above elements are reasonably accurate, the walking individual would be in approximate heat balance with a skin and clothing temperature of 37°C, conduction and convection exchange being zero, and evaporation just balancing heat production and radiation gain. Blum assumes that 43 per cent of the total solar radiation is reflected by the body and clothing, and that the terrain has an albedo of 0.25. It is obvious from this approximate analysis of the heat exchange under desert conditions that the solar load is large, and in the erect position at midday the surface of the head is the recipient of a considerable heat load.

During the war this subject was intensively studied in our laboratory. We designed a model human head of rubberized plastic material, heated internally by an electric bulb so as to produce a scalp temperature of 35°C at an environmental operative temperature of 21°C. On the top of the head was placed an artificial scalp of synthetic sponge covered with chamois cloth. A constant supply of water was fed to this scalp at a rate corresponding to warm but unstressed evaporation from the upper part of the human head (approximately 13 grams per hour). The vessel supplying this water, and the head itself, were mounted on separate platform scales so that total evaporation could be computed. The effect of a given atmospheric condition was determined (with various types of helmets) by record of the surface temperature of the scalp. The operative temperature was kept at about 38°C with a relative humidity of 25 per cent. Solar radiation was imitated by a 250-watt reflective drying lamp, with a filament temperature of about 2500°K, twelve inches above the top of the helmet; and air movement was produced by an electric fan six feet in front of the head yielding desired velocities.

The scalp, when no helmet was worn, showed about the same temperature as that of the room, with no simulated solar radiation and no air movement. With no solar radiation and with air movement, its temperature was about 2° below that of the room. With solar radiation, on the other hand, it rose to 20°C above room temperature with an air movement of about 100 cm./sec., and 22° to 28°C without air movement.

The general effect of wearing a tropical helmet is indicated in the table below.[116]

Mean crown temperature with helmet minus
crown temperature of unhelmeted head.

	No solar radiation	Solar radiation
Air movement	+1.0°	−11.7°
No air movement	+8.9°	− 3.8°

Thus, in the absence of solar radiation, the helmet actually does harm, interfering with normal heat loss to the atmosphere. In the presence of solar radiation it is slightly beneficial in still air and highly beneficial in moving air.

Experiments were also made with human subjects, and the concordance between these results and those obtained with the dummy head were close. In two series of experiments human subjects were used. In Series I an air-flow helmet was employed, somewhat similar to the hats worn by Chinese coolies, with considerable space between the helmet and the head for the passage of air. This helmet was treated with a single layer and with a double layer of the plastic material of which it was constructed, and in each case with and without the addition of aluminum foil. In the single-layer helmet, one

Scalp temperatures of human subjects
exposed to solar radiation.
(Operative temperature, 40°C, rel. hum. 25%)

	No air movement	Air movement, 200 cm./sec.
Single shell helmet	58.7	43.1
Single shell helmet plus foil	53.9	40.1
Double shell helmet	50.9	39.4
Double shell helmet plus foil	45.0	39.2

layer of aluminum foil was placed on its lower surface. With the double-layer helmet, two sheets of aluminum foil were placed facing each other in the interior of the space between the two plastic layers.

The results as reported by Shulman[116] are summarized on page 158.

In a second series, we used the ordinary plastic form-fitting helmet provided for our armed forces, with holes cut in it for ventilation (which we had found to be helpful in the absence of air movement but not in the presence of air movement). Operative temperatures were 38°C with air velocity of 100 cm./sec. The results are indicated below:

Scalp temperatures of human subjects
(Operative temperature, 38°C; R.H. 25%,
air velocity, 100 cm./sec.).

	No air movement	Air movement, 100 cm./sec.
Standard helmet, ventilated	51.6	46.2
Standard helmet plus an external layer of air-containing plastic material	43.6	39.4

It thus appears that, under conditions of solar heat and high air movement, which produce a scalp temperature of 43° to 46°C (with either standard or form-fitting helmets or helmets of the coolie type), the scalp temperature can be reduced by 4° to 7° by additional radiative or convective insulation under windy conditions; while in still air the gain may be 8° to 13°C.

In the design of helmets as well as in the design of other items of clothing, the relative efficiency of various materials in a number of specific physical properties is an important item in satisfactory performance. We have not attempted to review here the great detail of this field which includes measurements of air permeability, thermal conductance, weight per unit area, fiber volume, compressibility, elastic recovery from compression, hydroscopic capacity, and related items. An excellent discussion of these properties from the standpoint of comfort and efficiency has been recently completed by Fourt and Harris,[32] and will appear shortly in a survey publication.

General Conclusions

It seems obvious that the recently developed techniques of partitional calorimetry offer, for the first time, a sound basis for the basic study of the possibilities of clothing insulation: and that the concept of the clo value is likely to prove of value in the evaluation of results. It is equally clear, however, that such studies have only begun, and that their vigorous prosecution and extension is essential to fundamentally significant results. It has been shown that convective insulation depends primarily on the insulating value of the air contained within the clothing assembly, and that this factor is closely related to the weight and bulk of the assembly. Increase in insulation of this kind is limited by the fact that the addition of more clothing increases the area of the surface from which heat is lost to the environment, and that beyond a critical point additional layers of clothing are of minor value and may even increase total heat loss instead of decreasing it. At present, standard woolen clothing appears to be almost as effective as anything at our disposal. Certainly plastic materials which contain air within their fibers, and not merely between them, seem to offer promise; and it is quite possible that by the use of new fabrics and new combinations of the various layers in a clothing assembly, substantial improvements may be made.

The addition of special radiative insulation (copper or aluminum) also promise considerable increase in overall protective action against cold, particularly at high altitudes where the factor of radiative heat loss is relatively increased. Electrical heating appears a necessity for severe exposures, but radiative insulation is capable of providing equal insulation with less bulk, or of extending moderately the insulative value for comparable bulk.

In protection against hot environmental conditions, there are distinct possibilities of mitigating discomfort by the use of clothing with high radiative insulating power and also by the use of clothing which increases the surface susceptible to evaporative heat loss. Both of these procedures will be most effective in dry, hot climates, and there is no procedure now apparent for assistance in coping with the hot moist heat of the tropical jungle as a purely thermal factor.

There is a fertile field for research in the devising of protection of the extremities against chilling by better design of local convective insulation, and incorporation of radiation insulation in conjunction with artificial heat.

For protection against a hot, dry atmosphere, the standard tropical helmets now in use can be materially improved by a design which will increase air movement over the head (particularly in relatively still air), and by the use of radiative insulation.

All of these subjects deserve extended and basic research in the future. Readers interested in the field problems of human heat exchange emphasized in this chapter should not assume that the studies mentioned constitute a full survey of the valuable work of all investigators in this field, particularly during the war period. The available literature has been sampled for representative studies related to the work of our laboratory, but it would not have been difficult to illustrate the same problems by reference to the published work of a totally different set of investigators. Generally we have quoted investigators with whom we were in most immediate contact. Most of the points illustrated in this chapter could also have been documented from war period research in groups directed by E. F. Adolph, L. H. Newburgh, Willard Machle, and D. H. K. Lee. The investigations of Adolph and Newburgh, and their respective associates, are appearing in book form, and will be readily available. S. M. Horvath is currently publishing investigations made in association with the Machle group, and Craig Taylor has published several of his excellent investigations of heat tolerance times. The reviews of the past three years in the *Annual Reviews of Physiology* by John Brobeck, L. P. Herrington and A. P. Gagge, and D. H. K. Lee, will provide informative reference to the work of these particular investigators as well as to many other valuable studies which are not mentioned directly in this chapter, but which should be inspected by any reader with substantial interests in the field of thermal physiology.

THE OBJECTIVES
OF AIR CONDITIONING

Historical Background

WE HAVE already considered clothing as a primitive device for adaptation to man's thermal environment. When our ancestors began to dress themselves in the skins of slaughtered animals, however, they also took refuge from the rigors of cold climates in caves or in rough shelters made of sticks or stones. For this purpose, and for protection against predatory human and animal foes, the dwelling was evolved.

With the discovery of fire it became possible to supplement negative protection against external cold by positive heating of living spaces, and this principle was brought to a high degree of perfection by the Romans who devised the hypocaust, a somewhat elaborate system in which air heated outside the building was brought under the floor or behind the walls of each room through hollowed tiles. This method of heating, however, was forgotten after the fall of the Roman Empire; and in Europe the smoke from open fires or stoves was generally removed by chimneys, which appear to have become general in Italy during the fourteenth century.

Later developments are described in some detail in the Report of the New York State Commission on Ventilation.[95] The jacketed stove by which the dwelling was warmed by air drawn over the surface of an enclosed heater, was invented by Savot in France in 1624, and improved by Desaguliers in England and by Franklin in the United States.

Meanwhile, the possible danger of too little air change,

quite aside from the problem with which the early "smoke doctors" were concerned, was commonly recognized. In 1631, Charles the First of England ordered that no house be erected with rooms less than ten feet in height and that the windows be built higher than their width for ventilation.

The first use of mechanical power to provide ventilation was in mines, where the lack of oxygen was often a major problem. Agricola, in 1553, describes a rotary fan used for this purpose. Desaguliers in England (1727), Triewald in Sweden (1741), and Hales in England (1743), suggested similar devices for use in mines and in the holds of ships. Desaguliers also designed a fan system for the British House of Commons, and subsequent improvements made in that building in the early Nineteenth Century by Davy, de Chabannes, and Reid, form an important chapter in the history of air conditioning. The reason why fresh air was needed in occupied spaces remained, however, a mystery.

The most famous illustration of the evils of lack of ventilation is that of the Black Hole of Calcutta, which Professor F. S. Lee has described in the following pregnant sentences:

On one of the hottest of the hot nights in British India, a little more than one hundred and fifty years ago, Siraj-Uddaula, a youthful merciless ruler of Bengal, caused to be confined within a small cell in Fort William 146 Englishmen whom he had that day captured in a siege of the city of Calcutta. The room was large enough to house comfortably but two persons. Its heavy door was bolted; its walls were pierced by two windows barred with iron, through which little air could enter. The night slowly passed away, and with the advent of the morning death had come to all but a score of the luckless company. A survivor has left an account of horrible happenings within the dungeon, of terrible strugglings of a steaming mass of sentient human bodies for the insufficient air. Within a few minutes after entrance every man was bathed in a wet perspiration and was searching for ways of escape from the stifling heat. Clothing was soon stripped off. Breathing became difficult. There were vain onslaughts on the windows; there were vain efforts to force the door. Thirst grew intolerable and there were ravings for the water which the guards passed in between the bars, not from feelings of mercy, but only to witness in ghoulish glee the added struggles for impossible relief. Ungovernable confusion and turmoil and riot soon reigned. Men became delirious. If any found sufficient room to fall to the floor, it was only to fall to their death, for they were trampled upon, crushed, and buried beneath the fiercely desperate wave of frenzied humanity above. The strongest sought death, some by praying for the hastening of the end; some by heaping insults upon the guards to try to induce them to shoot. But all efforts for relief were in vain, until at last bodily and mental agony was followed by stupor. This tragedy of the Black Hole of Calcutta will ever remain as the most drastic demonstration in human history of the bondage of man to the air that surrounds him.

An almost equally famous instance of the acute effect of overcrowding is the accident which occurred on board the *Londonderry*, which left Sligo for Liverpool in December, 1848, with two hundred passengers. Lewes has described this tragedy in the following lines:

Stormy weather came on, and the captain ordered everyone to go below. The cabin for the steerage passengers was only 18 feet long, 11 feet wide, and 7 feet high. Into this small place the passengers were crowded; they would only have suffered inconvenience, if the hatches had been left open; but the captain ordered these to be closed, and—for some reason not explained—he ordered a tarpaulin to be thrown over the entrance to the cabin and fastened down. The wretched passengers were now condemned to breathe over and over again the same air. This soon became intolerable. Then occurred a horrible scene of frenzy and violence, amid the groans of the expiring and the curses of the more robust; this was stopped only by one of the men contriving to force his way on deck, and to alarm the mate, who was called to a fearful spectacle; seventy-two were already dead, and many were dying; their bodies were convulsed, the blood starting from their eyes, nostrils, and ears.

The beneficial effects of good air have been equally obvious to medical men from early times; and the gospel of fresh air has been crystallized into definite and effective form in the development of sanatorium treatment for tuberculosis. Dr,

Edward Trudeau went to Saranac in 1873 as a hopeless victim of consumption. All his friends were filled with horror at the idea of his going, practically alone, to die, as they believed, in the Adirondack wilderness, in a little town consisting of little more than a sawmill and half a dozen cabins, forty-two miles from a railroad. Dr. Trudeau did not die, however, during the winter of 1873, but grew much better; and some ten years later, as a result of his experience, he founded the Adirondack Cottage Sanatorium, which in its primitive form consisted of a single house in which, with great difficulty, he persuaded two consumptive patients to live. That was the beginning of the demonstration in this country of the fresh-air treatment of tuberculosis which Brehmer and others had introduced on the other side of the water. Since that day there has been a steady increase in the weight of evidence indicating that fresh air is one of the most valuable hygienic agents which may be utilized for the prolongation of human life and the strengthening of human vitality.

It was not until the present century that we learned what the important factors really were which determined the difference between "bad air" and "good air."

There are, in general, five different changes which take place in the air of an unventilated room as a result of human occupancy. Exactly the same effects are produced by gas flames or other processes of combustion, since the vital process is itself essentially a combustion, analogous to the burning of organic substances outside the body. Leaving out of consideration for the moment the special types of atmospheric pollution contributed by various industrial processes, these changes associated with deficient ventilation are as follows:

1. The oxygen content of the air is reduced.

2. The carbon dioxide content of the air is increased.

3. There is given off into the air a variable amount of partially oxidized organic matter. Much of this material is of nitrogenous nature such as the urea discharged in the perspiration. It is substances of this sort combined with aromatic

fatty compounds, chiefly derived from the skin and clothing, often partly from decomposition in uncared-for mouths, which we perceive as the "body odor" when we enter an unventilated room from the fresh outer air and which is almost always to be noticed in a gymnasium.

4. The temperature of the air is raised by the heat liberated in the course of the body oxidations.

5. The humidity of the air is increased by the moisture given off in the breath and from the skin.

It was natural that physiologists should first seek to explain the sensations experienced in a badly ventilated room by decrease in oxygen. When a mouse is confined in a bell-jar, it eventually dies of oxygen starvation and it seemed logical to assume that the same phenomenon occurred to a less degree in a badly ventilated room. As a matter of fact, men may sometimes die from oxygen starvation in a clogged sewer manhole or the lower parts of a mine, and the symptoms experienced on a high mountain peak or in an airplane are directly due to lack of oxygen.

By 1777, however, the great French chemist Lavoisier suggested that presence of carbon dioxide, rather than lack of oxygen, was the objectionable factor.[95] Claude Bernard in 1857, and Lewes in 1860 held this view. It was Pettenkofer in 1863 who pointed out that even the increase of carbon dioxide in a badly ventilated room was, quantitatively, quite inadequate to explain the results observed.

In rooms of ordinary construction and at normal altitude, the changes in oxygen and carbon dioxide, even with the worst ventilation, are found to be comparatively slight. The oxygen may fall from 21 to 20 per cent, and the carbon dioxide may rise from 0.03 to 0.5 per cent; greater changes than these are not observed even in the most crowded and worst ventilated rooms on account of the leakage through walls and ceilings and cracks of all sorts. Such values are very far from those which are found to produce harmful physiological effects. The air in the lungs under normal conditions contains 16 per

167

cent of oxygen and 5 per cent of carbon dioxide, and the respiratory apparatus easily accommodates itself to considerable variations in the composition of the atmosphere by slight automatic changes in the rate and depth of respiration so as to maintain the composition of the alveolar air unchanged. In mines the oxygen is often deliberately kept down to 17 per cent or less in the hope of avoiding the dust explosions that are likely to occur in freely ventilated mines during cold weather.

Some of the most interesting work along this line has been on the phenomena of mountain sickness. Henderson, Douglas, and Haldane made an important series of studies of this kind on Pike's Peak, where the partial pressure of oxygen present corresponds to about 13 per cent at ordinary atmospheric pressure. Under these conditions there are distinct symptoms of mountain sickness as a result of oxygen deficiency, blueness of the lips and face, loss of appetite, nausea and vomiting, intestinal disturbances, headache, fainting, periodic breathing, and great difficulty in getting breath on exertion. After a few days at such altitudes the symptoms began to lessen, and after a few weeks of acclimatization the extreme reactions disappear, although periodic breathing was still occasionally observed, and lips became blue on vigorous exertion.

Many people live active and vigorous lives under such conditions as this. In the great city of Potosi in the Andes, for instance, the partial pressure of oxygen is very close to that at Pike's Peak, and many famous resorts at an altitude of 5000 feet have a lower partial pressure of oxygen than obtains in the most crowded room.

Pettenkofer, in 1863, turned for an explanation to the third factor mentioned above, the presence of organic effluvia given off from the body; and, while he knew that the increase of carbon dioxide was not important in itself, he suggested the use of this substance as an index of the assumed harmful materials, since these hypothetical poisons and the carbon dioxide were given off from the human body and might be expected to vary together.

On this basis, it was possible to compute the amount of fresh air needed to correct the conditions in an overcrowded room. It was known that the human individual produces about 0.6 cubic feet of carbon dioxide per hour and that normal outdoor air contains 0.03 per cent of CO_2. It was assumed that 0.06 per cent of CO_2 in the atmosphere represented a permissible maximum figure. Therefore, by dividing 0.6 cubic foot by .0006 — .0003 (or .0003) the figure of 2000 cubic feet of air per person per hour was obtained as a desirable figure. Roughly, this corresponds to 30 cubic feet per minute per person; and this application of sound arithmetic to a defective basic theory led to the enactment of widespread legislation requiring that this amount of air be supplied in schools and other places of assembly. Furthermore, on the equally unsound assumption that ventilation could not be effected without undesirable drafts at a rate above three air changes per hour, standards of minimum space allowances per person were obtained by dividing 2000 by 3.

These well-meant but misguided standards cost millions of dollars in the aggregate and greatly retarded the development of adequate and efficient methods of air conditioning. The State of New York has only within the past five years freed itself from arbitrary restrictions of this type with respect to its schools, and laws based on the 30-cubic-feet formula are still in effect in many States.

The Modern Thermal Concept of Ventilation

In the latter decades of the nineteenth century the theory that the harmful effects of the air of an occupied room were due to the presence of specific poisonous materials given off in expired air was given major impetus by experiments of the French physiologist, Brown-Séquard. These experiments were shown to be faulty by many observations (reviewed in some detail by the New York State Commission), and in 1883

Hermans of Amsterdam demonstrated clearly that the air of a chamber containing only 15 per cent of oxygen and 2 to 4 per cent of carbon dioxide was not toxic and that the effects experienced in crowded rooms were not due to any chemical poisons but to heat and humidity. In spite of such evidence, the older chemical theory continued to prevail; and the senior author of the present volume was taught in the late nineties that the object of ventilation was to remove "anthropotoxin" or "morbific matter" contributed by the expired air.

But the studies of Flügge at Breslau in 1905 finally exorcised the specter of anthropotoxin. He and his pupils demonstrated that no discomfort was experienced in an experimental chamber in which the concentration of carbon dioxide had risen to over 1 per cent, if the chamber were kept cool. In a chamber with 1.1 per cent CO_2, a temperature of 30°C (86°F)* and a relative humidity of 87 per cent, the subject experienced great discomfort, which was not relieved by breathing fresh air from outside through a tube, but was completely relieved by cooling the chamber to 17°C (63°F) (although the CO_2 had meanwhile risen to 1.6 per cent). These German experiments were almost immediately repeated and confirmed by Benedict in the United States in 1907, and by Haldane and his associates in England. Their conclusions were embodied in British recommendations for the control of air conditions in cotton-weaving sheds in 1909. Similar studies were extended by Hill and his associates in England in 1913.

Thirty years ago it had been demonstrated beyond question that the following conclusions, enunciated by Flügge, were correct:

"1. Repeated experiments, on both normal and diseased subjects, made with precise experimental methods and with careful control of thermal conditions have demonstrated that

---

* In earlier chapters, dealing with primarily physiological problems, all temperatures have been cited in °C. In this and successive chapters, °F are also cited in parentheses, because these are the temperatures used in practice by the American Engineer. In a few tables only °F are used.

the chemical changes in the properties of the air produced in occupied spaces by the gaseous excreta of human beings, do not exert any harmful influence on the health of the occupants.

"2. When conditions detrimental to health are observable in closed and crowded rooms—such as headache, fatigue, dizziness, nausea, etc.—these symptoms are to be attributed solely to deficient heat loss.

"3. The thermal properties of our atmospheric environment —temperature, moisture, air movement—are of far greater significance for our well-being than the chemical properties of the air. The feelings of freshness which we experience when a closed room is freely ventilated or when we emerge into the outer air, are clearly due to more effective cooling of the body."

As F. S. Lee once put the case, the major problems of air conditioning are physical, not chemical—cutaneous, not respiratory.

These conclusions do not, of course, apply in a factory where specific poisonous gases or dusts are present in the atmosphere, or to a home in which defective heating or cooling appliances may liberate carbon monoxide.

Even in ordinary occupied spaces there is one other factor to be considered, the physiological effect of odors. This problem is far less important than the thermal one, but is not wholly negligible.

In the studies of the New York State Commission on Ventilation an extensive series of experiments were made on the effect of chemical vitiation upon appetite. Temperature conditions were kept uniformly constant and comfortable, but on some days fresh air was supplied, while on other days the air of the room was allowed to accumulate any chemical effluvia contributed by the occupants. A standard luncheon was served to the subjects in the chamber and the amount of food consumed was determined by weighing the amounts left on the plates. In four series of such experiments (each series including 71 to 100 meals) the excess of calories consumed on fresh-air days as compared with stale-air days was respectively 4.4,

6.8, 8.6, and 13.6 per cent. Comfort votes indicated no conscious preference for the fresh-air days (since persons present in a room while odors are slowly accumulating do not perceive the fact); but it seems apparent that the presence of body odors did interfere with the appetite for food.[148]

Winslow and Greenburg[135] exposed young guinea pigs to strong putrefactive odors from dog feces, with parallel controls. Fifteen series of experiments were conducted with 5 to 13 pairs of animals in each series. During the first 6 days of exposure, the control animals showed an excess of weight gain as compared with the animals exposed to the odor, amounting on the sixth day, to about 2 per cent. Later, the two series became more alike and after the fifteenth day no significant difference existed.

It thus appears that there may be a slight effect of odor upon the appetite for food. The air change necessary to avoid accumulation of body odors is, however, far below the limits set by older standards. Yaglou and his associates[150] studied this problem in an experimental booth and showed that only when subjects were crowded together so that less than 300 cubic feet of air were available per person were more than 7 to 11 cubic feet of fresh air per person per minute required to eliminate objectionable body odors. The *A.S.H.V.E. Guide*,[2] therefore, points out that with a space allotment of 400 cubic feet per person, only 1½ air changes per hour are necessary to provide an air change of 10 c.f.m. per person and that "in rooms occupied by only a few persons such a rate of air change will be automatically attained in cold weather by normal leakage." The conclusion is then drawn that "in the ordinary dwelling with adequate cubic space allotment, no special provision for controlling chemical purity is necessary (aside from removal of fumes from heating appliances)."

In larger occupied spaces "it is control of the thermal properties of the air in order to effect the removal of the heat produced by human bodies, rather than control of chemical properties, which must govern practice."

172

Influence of High Temperatures Upon the Physiological Status of the Body

The New York State Commission on Ventilation[95] made exhaustive studies on young clothed male human subjects under three atmospheric conditions, as follows: 20° (68.0°F) with 50 per cent relative humidity; 24° (75.2°F) with 50 per cent relative humidity; and 29.5° (86.0°F) with 80 per cent relative humidity. These studies have been reviewed in Chapter III, and their major results for one series of experiments are graphically indicated in Figure 24. It will be noted that in the cool room the rectal temperature fell during the day, while in the warm room it rose slightly and in the hot room rose more rapidly. The same was true of the pulse rate, except that at 75.2°F it fell slightly. The Crampton Index rose markedly in the cool room, rose slightly in the warm room, and markedly in the hot room.

Observations at a much wider range of temperatures were made at the Pittsburgh Research Laboratory of the American Society of Heating and Ventilating Engineers. They are summarized in the *A.S.H.V.E. Guide*[2] with references to the original papers. The following results were recorded for skin and rectal temperatures.

Effective Temp. of room*	Temperature of skin of cheek	Rise in rectal temperature
E.T.	°C	°C/hr.
70°F	—	0
80	35.6	0
85	35.9	0.06
90	36.1	0.07
95	36.4	0.50
100	37.6	1.20
105	40.4	2.20
110	—	3.30

* This item is explained on page 105

173

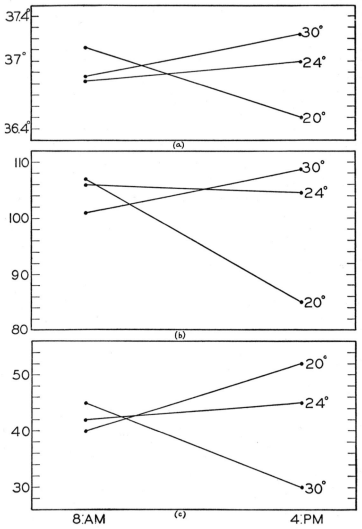

Figure 24. (a) Effect on body temperature, (b) pulse rate, and (c) Crampton Index (a measure of circulatory fitness) of eight hours at three levels of room temperature, 30°, 24°, and 20°C (68°, 75.2°, and 86°F).

Figure 25 shows the changes in body temperature and pulse rate for three different degrees of relative humidity at varying air temperatures.

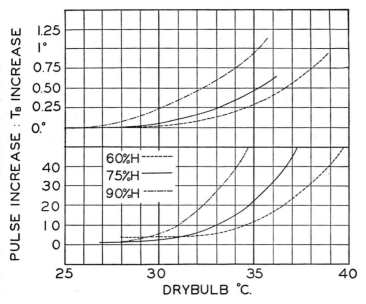

Figure 25. The effect of three hours of work in elevating pulse rate and body temperatures above normal levels at three levels of relative humidity. (Based on A.S.H.V.E. Research Laboratory Reports, 1938.)

The *Guide* effectively illustrates by a diagram the fact that rising body temperature, due to inadequate heat loss, is associated with

vasodilation,
increased circulation to the skin,
increased pulse rate,
temporary loss of blood volume,
circulatory insufficiency;

that the extreme sweating by which the body attempts to increase heat loss leads to

heat exhaustion,
dehydration of the body,

loss of body salts,

heat cramps;

and that failure to compensate effectively ultimately brings about progressive rise of body temperature, increase in metabolism, derangement of the regulatory centers, and heat stroke.

Studies made on soldiers marching (with packs) at a rate of three miles per hour showed that such work became impossible when the rectal temperature reached 39° (102°F) and the pulse rate reached 145.[29]

Valuable data on upper limits for possible activity have been provided by the English physiologists Haldane and Cadman.[23] These observers report that at 21° (70°F) wet bulb, soldiers marching in uniform are liable to heat stroke; that any exertion begins to be accompanied by depression above 25° (77°F) wet bulb; that at 26.5° (80°F) wet bulb "if clothes be removed and maximum body surface exposed, work can be done provided a current of air is available" (Cadman), but that hard and continuous work is impracticable even when the subject is stripped to the waist (Haldane). At 29.5° (85°F) wet bulb, "only light work is possible" (Cadman). Above 31° (89°F) wet bulb, "in fairly still air the body temperature begins to rise, even in the case of persons stripped to the waist and doing no work; when once started this rise continues until symptoms of heat stroke arise" (Haldane). The rationale of this phenomena has been made clear in Chapter III.

Relation of Thermal Conditions to Efficiency

With degrees of environmental overheating far below such extreme conditions as most of those mentioned above, the circulatory reactions which accompany the attempt to maintain heat equilibrium are accompanied by sensations of discomfort (as pointed out in Chapter III); and also by a definite falling-off in the physical work performed under a given stimulus. The New York State Commission on Ventilation conducted a highly significant study on this point. Groups of subjects were kept in the experimental chamber under four different conditions: 20° (68°F) with a fresh-air supply of 45 c.f.m. per person; 20° (68°F) with stagnant air; 24° (75°F) with the fans on; and 24° (75°F) with stagnant air. In all cases relative humidity was between 49 and 54 per cent. For two work-periods of one hour, each of the subjects lifted a 5-pound iron dumbbell through a distance of 2¼ feet as many times as he chose, with no urging from the observer, but with a small incentive bonus (beyond his regular salary) on the basis of the amount of work performed, as recorded by an automatic counter. Thus a modest piece-work incentive was supplied. The results, for four subjects over a period of 20 days, were as follows:

Condition	Cool plus air	Cool stagnant	Warm plus air	Warm stagnant
Foot pounds of work	26,711	24,359	22,771	20,481

The maximum figure of 26,711 foot pounds was reduced 9 per cent in the cool stagnant air, 15 per cent in the warm air with air movement, and 23 per cent in the warm stagnant air. In a maximal-effort test at 30° (86°F) with 80 per cent relative humidity, the reduction as compared with 20° (68°F) was 28 per cent, but conditions here were less rigorously controlled. It may be assumed that the influence of the fresh air introduced in the first and third series of experiments was primarily due to the cooling effect of air movement. It is a striking fact that an increase in air temperature from 20° (68°F) to 24° (75°F) plus elimination of air movement should cut production down by nearly one-quarter (even with moderately low relative humidity).

Other carefully planned and controlled series of experiments were made with clerical work (typing) and purely mental work (addition, cancellation, and mental multiplication). Ignoring certain minor differences in detail (which showed no significant deviations) the mean results of six series of experiments were as follows:

| Condition | Performance Score | | |
	Addition and cancellation	Mental multiplication	Typing
20° (68°F) 50% R.H.	112	120	301
24° (75°F) 50% R.H.	112	131	287

Results in addition and cancellation were identical under the two atmospheric conditions. Mental multiplication was 9 per cent better in the warm room, typewriting 5 per cent better in the cool room. Whether these latter results are significant is doubtful; five out of six experiments showed better results for mental multiplication in the hot room, possibly as the Commission suggests, because "purely mental work may be considered as perhaps furnishing a certain amount of distraction under uncomfortable atmospheric conditions." In any case, it is clear that purely mental work is not hampered by a temperature of 24° (75°F).

The A.S.H.V.E. experiments at Pittsburgh gave the following significant results of a series of experiments in which effective temperature was varied, with work done at a rate of 90,000 foot-pounds per hour.

Effective temperature	Total work in foot-pounds	Rise in rectal temperature, °F per hour	Increase in pulse rate, beats per min. per hour.
60°	225,000	0.0	6
70°	225,000	0.1	7
80°	209,000	0.3	11
85°	190,000	0.6	17
90°	153,000	1.2	31
95°	102,000	2.3	61
100°	67,000	4.0	103
105°	49,000	6.0	158
110°	37,000	8.5	237

At 60° and 70°F Effective Temperature the subjects could work for two hours with no important rise in body temperature or pulse rate. At 80° and 85°F they could also work for two hours, but with slight increases (which would ultimately have become significant) in rectal temperature and pulse rate. Above this point both temperature and heart rate increased rapidly; and above 100° the subjects could stand it for less than half an hour. McConnell and Yagloglou, who participated in these experiments,[78] reported that, taking a temperature of 32° (90°F) with 30 to 60 per cent relative humidity as a base line, production was cut in half by an increase of humidity to the saturation point and by a rise in temperature of 1° (2°F), or by an increase to 43° (110°F) with 60 per cent relative humidity, or to 51° (125°F) with 30 per cent relative humidity.

Highly significant data on this point have been accumulated by British authorities under actual working conditions in industrial establishments. Vernon[123] studied production in tinplate mills (where the process itself involves the production of a high degree of artificial heat), comparing mills with various types of ventilation during the winter and summer seasons.

Factory	Type of ventilation	Relative output Dec.–Jan.	July–Aug.	Per cent reduction in summer
A	Good, artificial	100.5	97.5	3.0
B	Moderately good, artificial	102.5	97.0	6.4
C	Moderately good, artificial	105.3	94.5	10.4
D	Good, natural	104.5	93.0	11.0
E	Poor, natural	108.0	93.5	13.4

Vernon[125] also cites striking results of a study of 138 coal miners, made by recording at various temperatures the amount of time they rested and the time it took to fill a hod with coal.

Temperature, °F wet bulb	dry bulb	Pulse increase beats/min.	Minutes to fill in tub	Rate of coal production
70.1	65.6	6.7	8.6	94
73.3	66.0	7.3	8.0	100
80.8	74.1	10.0	9.2	82
81.7	73.6	9.0	8.5	91
82.4	76.2	11.1	9.1	81
86.2	79.3	22.4	9.6	59

Thus, it appears that between 26° (81°F) and 28° (82°F) there is a falling off of 10 to 15 per cent in production, and at 30° (86°F) a decrease of over 40 per cent.

Another English worker, Weston,[67] reports that in cotton weaving sheds production begins to fall off when the wet-bulb temperature exceeds 24° (75°F).

Missenard[80] cites Hasse in Germany as recording a deviation of 25 per cent in production by miners as a result of an increase in temperature from 18° (64°F) to 30° (86°F); and

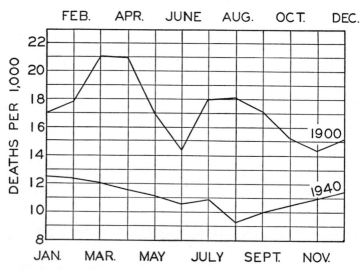

Figure 26. Death rate by month from all causes for 1900 and 1940 (based on Death Registration States of 1900).

Liberson, in France, as reporting a falling off of 50 per cent in work capacity (in a task much less arduous than mining) with an increase in temperature from 18° (64°F) to 33° (91°F).

Relation of Atmospheric Conditions to Respiratory Disease

One of the most striking phenomena of epidemiology, perhaps the most outstanding problem of epidemiology in countries of the Temperate and Frigid Zones, is the seasonal variation in the incidence of respiratory disease. This subject will be discussed in some detail in Chapter VII, but the major elements in the picture may be briefly summarized here.

Figure 26 shows the death rate from all causes in the Death Registration States of 1900, for that year and for the year 1940, by months. The actual figures are as follows:

Deaths Per 1000 Population, Registration States of 1900

	1900	1940	Decrease		1900	1940	Decrease
Jan.	17.0	12.5	4.5	July	18.0	10.9	7.1
Feb.	17.8	12.4	5.4	Aug.	18.1	9.3	8.8
Mar.	21.1	12.1	9.0	Sept.	17.2	10.0	7.2
Apr.	20.8	11.6	9.2	Oct.	15.3	10.5	4.8
May	17.0	11.2	5.8	Nov.	14.4	11.0	3.4
June	14.4	10.6	3.8	Dec.	15.2	11.5	3.7

It will be noted that in 1900 the curve showed two sharp peaks, in March and April, and in July and August, these peaks being undoubtedly related to the influence of season upon temperature conditions favorable to the transmission of germs causing intestinal diseases (diarrhea, typhoid fever, and the like) and lowering the resistance of the human body to such diseases, in summer; and to conditions favoring the spread of the germs of respiratory diseases (such as pneumonia) and lowering resistance to such diseases, in winter. The improvement of infant feeding, the pasteurization of milk, and the control of typhoid fever and related diseases have now wiped out

181

the summer peak entirely; while advances in control of respiratory diseases, immunization procedures, and improved methods of therapy have cut off the top of the winter peak. The earlier figures show clearly, however, how serious may be the influence of extreme climatic conditions on human health, and the months between January and March still present serious hazards of this kind.

That the high winter incidence of colds, influenza, and pneumonia is directly related to lowering of the vital resistance of the upper respiratory tract due to atmospheric conditions, there can be no reasonable doubt. How far it is the result of a chilling outdoor atmosphere in itself or to the sharp contrast between that outdoor environment and our overheated interiors, we do not know; but it seems possible that too sharp a contrast is an important factor in the picture. The Romans were aware of this factor; Seneca in *De Providentia* says, "The man who has always had glazed windows to shield him from a draught, whose feet have been kept warm by hot applications renewed from time to time, whose dining-halls have been tempered by hot air passing beneath the floor and circulating round the walls, this man will run great risk if he is brushed by a gentle breeze."

The first concrete suggestion as to the mechanism by which such a contrast between indoor and outdoor conditions may operate came from the English physiologist, Leonard Hill. Hill and Muecke,[59] in 1913, by direct observation with the nasal speculum, observed that the mucous membranes of the nose became swollen and red in warm moist air, and that there was a marked increase in secretion. On passing from the warm to cold air he found that the mucous membrane became paler, but still remained swollen. He believed that this condition predisposed to disease for the reason that the defensive mechanism of the blood, the immunization properties of the plasma, the cleansing action of the cilia, and the phagocytic action of the white blood cells were all diminished by the cold, while the pathogenic bacteria found a suitable nidus for their growth

182

in the secretion of the swollen mucous membranes. He found that keeping the air in motion in warm rooms very materially interfered with the hyperemic effect, and believed that in this way the massiveness of direct infection was reduced. He also observed that warm dry air produced less swelling and secretion than warm moist air.

The New York Commission extended these investigations in an exhaustive study of the effect of atmospheres ranging from 10° (50°F) to 30° (86°F) upon the color and secretion of the mucous membranes and the swelling of the turbinates. The latter phenomenon was observed by the use of the Glatzel mirror, a cold polished metal surface held just below the nose immediately above the upper lip. Normal expiration through the nose produces a deposit of moisture on the metal surface and the outline of this moisture deposit, traced with a beeswax pencil, gives a very clear picture of the extent of expiration through each nostril. Figure 27 shows one case in which both nostrils showed normal results in a room at 20° (68°F) with reduction, for both, to about a quarter of their normal expiration at 27° (80°F). The other subject represented had an occluded right nostril and a very open left nostril at 20° (68°F). In his case, the expiration from the right nostril almost disappeared at 27° (80°F). Many individual differences in response occurred; but on the whole it seemed clear that on passing from a normal or cold atmosphere into a hot atmosphere there was a strong general tendency for swelling of the inferior turbinates and increased redness and moistness of the nasal mucosa. When a strong air current was directed against the face of the subject in a cold atmosphere, a significant result was commonly observed. Under these conditions, the membranes became anemic (as shown by pallor), but swelling and secretion increased, a condition which would appear particularly favorable to microbic invasion. It was also found by the Commission that industrial workers exposed to extremes of temperature showed a very high proportion of atrophic rhinitis. Of 58 students, only 3 per cent showed this condition; of 27 outdoor workers, 19 per cent; of 26 boiler room operators and the like, exposed to dry heat, 35 per cent; and of 32 laundry workers exposed to a hot, moist environment, 63 per cent. The nasal membranes of the workers with atrophic rhinitis reacted abnormally to changes in experimental atmospheres, failing, under ordinary conditions of chilling (as the control subjects did under extreme conditions of cold or draft) to show the protective mechanism of diminished swelling and secretion on exposure to cold.

Such effects may undoubtedly be aggravated by localized drafts, although that is a subject on which our knowledge is

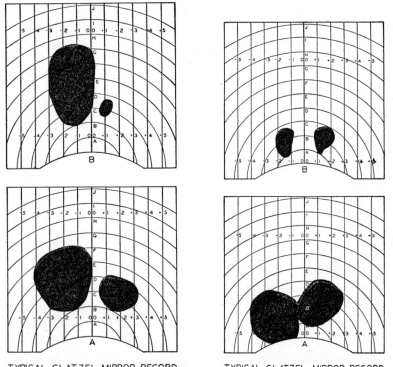

TYPICAL GLATZEL MIRROR RECORD
CHANGE FROM NORMAL TO HOT CONDITION

TYPICAL GLATZEL MIRROR RECORD
CHANGE FROM NORMAL TO HOT CONDITION

Figure 27. Glatzel mirror records of occluding effects of passage from normal (20°C, 68°F) atmosphere A to warm (27°C, 80°F) atmosphere B, in two subjects.

meager. Azzi[4] in Italy showed that chilling the hand by resting it on a piece of ice, or directing a fan on the shoulders or back, might cause a drop in the temperature of the tracheal mucosa of 0.4 to 0.6° (1°F). In this country Mudd and his coworkers[89] made more elaborate studies of the influence of chilling upon the physiological status of the upper respiratory tract. These observers chilled their subjects by removing wraps and by applying cold wet towels to the back or by turning an electric fan upon the back. In all cases they found that chilling caused not "congestion" of the mucosa (as is often assumed), but the reverse. Reduction in the local blood supply to the oropharynx and the soft palate was always demonstrated by decreased temperature of the surfaces in question as recorded by a delicate thermopile. While, in such experiments, the skin temperature fell from 32.5° to 30° (90.5° to 86.0°F), the temperature of the mucous surfaces fell from 34° to 29° (93° to 84°F); and, what was still more striking, the recovery from such ischemia was very slow. After the fan was turned off and wraps were restored, the temperature of the oral mucosa rose, but for periods of 20 to 30 minutes it remained 2° (3.5°F) below its original normal value. The authors comment as follows: "In the insufficient light of present knowledge, it would seem not improbable that the ischemia incident on cutaneous chilling, by decreasing cell respiration, or by retarding removal of the products of cell metabolism, or by increasing the permeability of the epithelial cell surfaces to the bacterial products, or by decreasing the local supply of specific antibodies, or by altering the media in the tonsillar crypts and folds of the pharyngeal and nasal mucosa in which the bacteria are living, or, especially when accompanied by direct chilling of the mucous membrane, by altering the state of aggregation of the colloids of the protoplasm, or by a combination of these factors might effect the local change postulated by Wright and thus so disturb the equilibrium between host and parasite as to excite infection."

Winslow and Greenburg confirmed the general results of

Mudd, but obtained further data on the effects of drafts (400 to 1700 feet per minute) directed on the head and feet, respectively. A draft on the head alone caused a drop of 2° to 5° (4° to 9°F) in the temperature of the nasal mucosa. On the other hand, a draft on the feet caused a 1° to 2° (2° to 4°F) reflex *rise* in the temperature of the nasal mucosa. The oral mucosa showed similar changes, though they were less marked. When chilled by a draft on the head, recovery—as in Mudd's study—was very slow. Fifteen minutes to half-an-hour after the draft was discontinued, the nasal mucosa still remained a degree or so below its normal temperature.[136]

It seems clear from common experience of the seasonal prevalence of upper respiratory diseases that exposure to chilling—either general or local—definitely tends toward increasing susceptibility to infections of this type; and it is probable that ischemia of the nasal and oral surfaces plays an important role in the picture. It seems possible that habituation to unduly high indoor temperatures may increase the harmful effects of a cold outdoor environment, although this conclusion is less certain.

The "Ideal" Temperature

It is obvious that temperature conditions far above the optimum make active physical work difficult or impossible and, when extreme, produce fatal results. It is equally clear that conditions far below the optimum increase the liability to respiratory diseases and, beyond certain limits, lead to death from chilling. Between such extremes there must be an ideal optimum for health and comfort. What is this optimum?

At first sight, the evidence on this point seems somewhat conflicting. The early studies of the New York State Commission on Ventilation[95] seemed to point to an air temperature of 20° (68°F) as ideal for conditions in the schoolroom. This conclusion was based on comfort votes of subjects in the experimental rooms of the Commission, which showed that either 20° (68°F) or 24° (75°F) was definitely preferred to

186

30° (86°F); and the fact that the performance of physical work was reduced at 24° (75°F) as compared with 20° (68°F); and by votes of observers and teachers and students in the schoolrooms which seemed to indicate a preference for the range between 18.5° (65°F) and 22° (72°F).

Our most extensive data on this subject are those derived from the studies embodied in the Comfort Chart of the American Society of Heating and Ventilating Engineers.[2] This chart, as pointed out in Chapter III, is based on a large number of comfort votes which indicate ranges of Effective Temperature corresponding in winter and in summer to the combinations of air temperature and relative humidity for which preference was expressed. The mid-point of the winter comfort zone comes at an Effective Temperature of 66°F and that of the summer comfort zone at an Effective Temperature of 71°F. The air temperatures corresponding to these Effective Temperatures at certain degrees of relative humidity are as indicated below, to the nearest Fahrenheit degree.

Effective Temperature °F	Air Temperature, °F				
R.H. =	10%	30%	50%	70%	90%
66°	74°	72°	70°	68°	67°
71°	82°	78°	76°	73°	72°

Thus, allowing for the two factors of relative humidity and seasonal acclimatization (and clothing), we have a range of ideal air temperatures from 19° (67°F) to 28° (82°F).

More recently, a careful study of the sensations of workers in air-conditioned offices by Rowley, Jordan, and Snyder[112] has thrown serious doubt on the validity of the Comfort Chart in the area of moderately low temperatures. Our own physiological studies, long ago, led us to doubt the extent of the influence of relative humidity in this temperature zone.[141]

Rowley's data indicate that at air temperatures between 21° (70°F) and 25.5° (78°F) relative humidity had very little effect upon sensations of comfort, and that the ideal indoor condition for office workers in summer was 23.5° (74°F) (70 per cent of the subjects voting "ideal," about 15 per cent too cool, and about 15 per cent too warm).

The diversity of the findings is altogether understandable when the complexity of the factors involved is kept in mind. The following table, for example, illustrates the influence of air movement and metabolism as given by Gagge, Burton, and Bazett,[35] and by our own experimental data, in °F for subjects with average clothing.

| | | Air temperature for thermal balance, °F | | | |
| | | Seated at Rest | Level Walking | | |
Conditions	Air movement		Slow	Medium	Fast
Normal, indoors	20 f.p.m.	70	58	43	28
Drafty, indoors	100 f.p.m.	75	60	46	30
Normal, outdoors	5 m.p.h.	76	61.5	47	33
Windy, outdoors	20 m.p.h.	78	63	48	35

At least six important modifying variables are involved in the "ideal" air temperature, as follows:

Environmental factors	Individual factors
Radiative effects	Metabolism
Air movement	Clothing
Vertical temperature differences	Acclimatization

We omit relative humidity from this list because its influence is so slight at otherwise favorable temperature conditions.

The laboratory studies of the New York State Commission and the American Society of Heating and Ventilating Engineers were carried out in experimental rooms, with walls at the same temperature as the air, so that air temperature was the same as true operative temperature. Schoolroom studies and office studies, on the other hand, involve one or more cold walls which substantially influence heat loss from the body. Thus, if we assume that air temperatures and wall temperatures exert equal influence on operative temperature (which is approximately the case with minimal air movement), and if we assume a cubical room with one outside wall at 13° (55°F) and all inside surfaces at air temperature, an operative temperature of 21° (70°F) would be produced by a temperature of air and five internal surfaces of 21.7° (12 × 21 — 13 ÷ 11), or 71.5°F. If there were two cold walls (as might happen in a corner room), the temperature of air and inner walls would have to be raised to 22.6° (73°F).

The influence of air movement has been indicated in earlier chapters, but it does not enter in material degree under normal indoor environments. Vertical temperature differences may be important, if one relies on a single thermometer, since in badly heated or ventilated rooms, there may be a 5° to 9° (10° to 15°F) differential between floor and ceiling air.

The major factor, on the human side, is metabolic activity, as will be indicated in a succeeding paragraph. Variations in clothing and in acclimatization are also of major importance. It is probable that the relatively low optimum temperatures reported by the New York State Commission were related to these factors. Thirty years ago the average home was less well heated than today, and clothing, on the average was much heavier. Many of the present generation can recall the family crises in fall and spring when "winter woolies" were assumed and discarded, a practice almost unknown today. The lower temperatures preferred in England are similarly related to clothing habits and acclimatization.

The problem becomes greatly simplified and the apparently conflicting results are readily reconciled when the objectives to be attained are visualized in precise physiological terms.

Gagge and the writers[38] have shown that ideal comfort is experienced when three conditions are maintained:

A skin temperature of 33° (91.5°F),

A minimal heat change in the body tissues,

A minimal evaporative rate.

For the resting nude subject these three desiderata were fulfilled at an operative temperature of 30° (86°F), for the normally clothed subject at about 26° (78°F), for subjects in a semi-reclining position and almost completely at rest for a period of several hours. Air movement was minimal. Above this point sweat secretion increased. Below this point negative heat change increased. Both above and below, sensations of discomfort were recorded.

While no work experiments were made in this series, it is possible to predict, from the data at different operative temperatures, what would happen with varying metabolic rates. At a temperature of 23.3° (74°F) for the clothed subjects there was a negative heat change of 7 kilogram calories. This would be balanced by an increase in metabolism of 7 kilogram calories, an increase of 14 per cent over the actual recorded figure of 50 calories per square meter of body surface of the resting subject, which would be just what might be expected for subjects engaged in normal office activities, and checks exactly with Rowley's comfort votes.

Sherman estimates an increase of 40 per cent of resting metabolism for rapid typing. This would balance a negative heat change of 20 kilogram calories per square meter of body surface. We observed a negative heat change of 21.5 kilogram calories at 18.9° (68°F), so that for a metabolism of 70 kilogram calories per square meter, balance would be reached at that operative temperature, which is the New York State Commission optimum. So that, depending on physical activity, we find close concordance between physiological prediction and practical experience. The normally clothed individual in a state of complete rest needs (with no differential radiative effects and minimal air movement) an air temperature of 26°

(78°F). This is why, when one lies down for a rest, a comforter is appreciated. For moderate indoor activity the desirable figure drops to 23° (74°F). For more vigorous work (such as rapid typewriting) it falls to 20° (68°F). For very active work (corresponding to fast walking) it may be much lower, as suggested in the table on page 188.

So far as the various physical factors in the environment are concerned, it is obvious that complete prediction of thermal influences upon the body requires knowledge of all the four factors of air temperature, air movement, relative humidity, and mean radiant temperature. The Housing Commission of the Health Organization of the League of Nations[64] rightly urged that, in careful studies, all four of these variables should be recorded by the following four types of instruments, or others yielding similar data:

a. Silvered dry-bulb thermometers or hair-pin thermometers (Bargeboer).

b. Silvered dry-bulb katathermometers or the hot-wire anemometer.

c. Psychrometer, wet and dry bulb, whirling or ventilated.

d. Globe thermometer (Vernon) or the dry resultant thermometer (Missenard).

Various attempts have been made to combine two or more of these factors in a single index. Thus, the A.S.H.V.E.'s "Effective Temperature" attempts to represent the combined effect of air temperature and relative humidity. The basis of weighting is purely empirical and, as pointed out above, open to criticism as to its validity in the zone of optimum comfort. "Operative Temperature" represents the combined influence of air temperature and mean radiant temperature, and is derived from basic physical principles. British experts in this field use an "Equivalent Temperature" which takes into account air temperature, air movement, and radiation. French authorities employ a scale of "Resultant Temperatures" which is assumed to represent all four factors. Since the reactions of the body to each of the factors involved varies so widely at different points on the temperature range in its adaptive mechanisms of change in skin temperature and sweat secretions, it seems doubtful whether such attempts at simplification of the problem can meet with complete success.

Under ordinary indoor conditions, however, we are fortunate in the fact that air movement is generally minimal and relative humidity (in cold weather) generally low. Furthermore, differences between air temperature and mean radiant temperature are commonly slight. Where these conditions exist, the air temperature is the main determining factor in comfort; and that is precisely why the ordinary air thermometer is used, and will continue to be used, with success. In summer, when humidity may be high, this factor cannot be neglected. Here, the "Effective Temperature," which appears to be reliable in the zone of evaporative cooling, is useful. Similarly, in rooms with large exterior wall surfaces and considerable window areas, the concept of "Operative Temperature" must be invoked.

For ordinary indoor winter conditions, the adjustment of air temperature to metabolic activity is the major issue involved.

The Committee on the Hygiene of Housing of the American Public Health Association[22] in its first report suggested that in the ordinary home (with minimal air movement) 24° (75°F) might be a reasonable figure. With one cold wall, this would give an Operative Temperature of 1° to 2°F lower. The report suggested that, with the vertical variations common in the ordinary dwelling, the knee-high temperature should be 21° (70°F), with a temperature of perhaps 24.5° (76°F) at the 5-foot level, and a mean air temperature of 23.5° (74°F), corresponding perhaps to an operative temperature of 22° (72°F). This would correspond to normal household activities, but for very young children playing on the floor or for old people these temperatures should be increased by perhaps 1.5° (3°F). Later reports of the Committee will also emphasize the importance of reducing vertical differences in temperature as far as possible. It is suggested that the 6-inch temperature should not be more than 1.5° (3°F) below the 18-inch temperature, and the 6-foot temperature should not exceed the 18-inch temperature by more than the same amount.

In crowded auditoriums, where the occupants are surrounded by human bodies which cut off radiative heat loss, the temperature for comfort would be materially lower; and in work shops where metabolism is high it should be reduced far below this level. The New York State Commission found that in a gymnasium, even for almost nude subjects, a temperature of 13° to 18° (56° to 65°F) was preferred.

The Influence of Dry Air on the Membranes of the Nose and Throat

The influence of excessively dry air upon the nasal and oral mucosa remains to be considered. We have seen that variations in atmospheric humidity have little influence on purely thermal interchanges at low and moderate temperatures, and that a dry atmosphere is more desirable than a moist one at high temperatures. On the other hand, there is clear evidence that extremely dry climates and seasons are associated with increased mortality rates (as will be indicated in Chapter VII), and ill effects have been often popularly attributed to harmful influences upon the nose and throat by schoolroom air "dry as the Desert of Sahara."

The work of a number of early European investigators, as summarized in a paper from the John B. Pierce Laboratory of Hygiene,[146] has shown that, whatever the temperature and humidity of the inspired air (within reasonable limits), the temperature of the expired air is 33° to 34° (91° to 93°F) and its relative humidity is 90 to 98 per cent. The subject has recently been studied more exhaustively by Seeley.[114] He finds that in cold air (−8°C or 18°F) the temperature of the expired air may fall to 27° (−3°C) and its humidity to 79 per cent. At very high temperatures (54°C or 129°F) the expired air rose to 39° (95°F) and the relative humidity fell in one instance to 67 per cent. But within a range representing indoor temperatures (21° to 33°C or 69° to 91°F), the temperature of the expired air was between 32° and 35° (90° to 95°F), and this air was over 90 per cent saturated. This expired air contained about 36 grams of moisture per cubic foot. It is clear from all these studies that the drying influence of the atmosphere upon the membranes of the nose and throat depends upon the absolute moisture content of that atmosphere and not upon its relative humidity.

In our own laboratory we have devised a means of actually recording the degree of moisture present on the surface of the oral mucosa. A circular disc of standard white blotting paper at the end of a pin was dried and weighed in a weighing bottle. The pin was picked up by a steel cylinder with an internal screw clamp and applied in firm contact to the back of the throat just below the tip of the uvula of a subject, at one-hour intervals, while the subject was exposed to a given atmospheric condition. After 5 seconds of application, the cylinder was withdrawn and the pin and blotting paper replaced in the weighing bottle and weighed once more. Four air temperatures were studied (10°, 15.5°, 21° and 26.5°C or 50°, 60°, 70°, and 80°F), with relative humidities ranging at various temperatures from 16 per cent to 90 per cent. Altogether 220 records were obtained from four different subjects.[146]

The amount of moisture taken up by the blotting paper from the oral mucosa proved, as expected, to be related not to atmospheric temperature or relative humidity but to the absolute humidity of the atmosphere. The mean results are summarized in Figure 28, plotted against atmospheric vapor pressure.

With a vapor pressure of 0.40 inch of mercury and above, the surface of the oral mucosa is relatively moist but the observed figure varies from a moderately high to a very high figure. The sharp drop at a vapor pressure of 0.50 to 0.59 inch corresponds to the point at which active sweat secretion begins and suggests a reflex action of the vasomotor system.

On the other hand, at vapor pressures below 0.40 inch there is evident a marked drying of the oral mucosa.

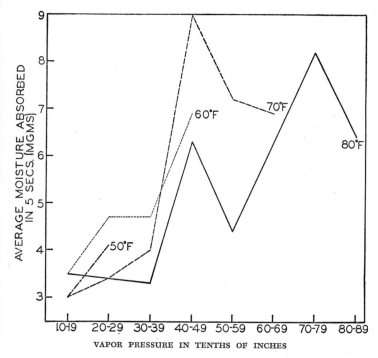

Figure 28. Average moisture absorbed from the oral mucosa of four subjects after three hours exposure to six different vapor pressures at the indicated temperatures.

Two important practical conclusions emerge from these studies.

In the first place, since the drying of the mucosa is due to absolute and not relative humidity, the air of the schoolroom in winter is no more harmful in its effect with 10 per cent relative humidity at 21° (70°F) than it is when the child is outdoors in saturated air at a temperature of —10° (14°F).

195

In the second place, since the critical point for drying of the oral mucosa is at about 0.40 inch of vapor pressure, it appears that drying of the mucosa must occur at air temperatures below 11.5° (53°F) with any moisture content; at a temperature of 15.5° (60°F) with less than 77 per cent relative humidity; at a temperature of 21° (70°F) with less than 54 per cent relative humidity; and at a temperature of 26.5° (80°F) with less than 39 per cent relative humidity.

Whether the drying out of the mucosa is actually harmful has not been clearly demonstrated. In any case, however, it is clear that it cannot be avoided when outdoors in cold dry winter weather, and that in such weather it cannot be avoided indoors without a very high degree of humidification. Sharp contrast effects under such conditions might well be worse than exposure to dry air, both indoors and out.

Summary of the Objectives of Air Conditioning

Air conditioning is defined in the *A.S.H.V.E. Guide* as: "The simultaneous control of all or at least the first three of those factors affecting both the physical and chemical conditions of the atmosphere within any structure. These factors include temperature, humidity, motion, distribution, dust, bacteria, odors, and toxic gases, most of which affect in greater or lesser degree human health or comfort."

The control of dust and toxic gases may be of major importance in many industrial processes, but it is not ordinarily significant in homes, offices, or places of assembly (provided that carbon monoxide is not given off by defective heating or cooking appliances). The presence of marked body odors is, however, of real importance. Such odors can be controlled by an air change of 10 cu. ft./min./person, and such a change will normally occur, during weather when windows must be closed, by normal leakage through the building structure. If new methods of construction involve the use of more impervious types of structures, some special means of air change may be required.

The reduction of the bacterial content of the air (by ultraviolet light or the use of aerosols) is now a common practice in the hospital operating room, the contagious pavilion, and many pediatric wards. Its role in schools, barracks, and places of public assembly is still in an experimental stage. Its application to other occupied spaces is not likely to be profitable.

The major universal problems of air conditioning are still air temperature, mean radiant temperature, relative humidity, and air movement. In indoor spaces, reduction of relative humidity and increase of air movement are essential for maximum comfort in hot weather. In cold weather, indoor relative humidity and air movement are generally low, and air temperature and mean radiant temperature are the factors of chief significance.

The physiological objective to be attained is clearly defined. It is fixed by the maintenance of a skin temperature of 33° (91°F) with minimal negative heat exchange and minimal evaporation of sweat. With the ordinary winter clothing worn in the Northern United States, this condition will be obtained, with varying degrees of metabolism at about the following temperatures in °F.

	Operative temperature	Air temperature (assuming a cold wall)
Complete rest	78°	79°–80°
Moderate activity	74°	75°–76°
Considerable activity (rapid typewriting)	68°	69°–70°

Much lower temperatures will be required for very active physical exertion. With summer clothing and summer acclimatization, the comfort temperatures at 30 per cent relative humidity may be several degrees higher; but in this area relative humidity is important and an effective temperature of 70° (air temperature, 70°F with 100 per cent relative humidity or 73°F with 60 per cent relative humidity or 77°F with 30 per cent relative humidity) will be reasonably comfortable.

C H A P T E R V I

METHODS OF AIR CONDITIONING

A TECHNICAL discussion of the design of heating appliances, of refrigerating machinery, of ventilation ducts and the like would be far beyond the compass of this book, but it does seem desirable here to review some of the broad principles of air conditioning* and to discuss the general methods available for maintaining thermal comfort. Such an analysis must begin with consideration of certain basic factors in the placement and construction of the structure in which air conditioning is to take place.

Orientation

The first of these factors, one of major importance, is the location of a proposed building with relation to the reception of solar heat and protection from (or exposure to) prevailing winds.

The importance of insolation has been fully realized only in recent years. Since the sun follows a relatively low daily arc through the heavens in winter, exposure in a southerly direction leads to maximum absorption of solar heat at this season. In summer, on the other hand, the sun at noon is more nearly overhead; and therefore at this season a generally

---

* T. Bedford of the British Medical Research Council, who is well known for his many contributions to the field of ventilating and heating hygiene, has recently written a valuable text which surveys these problems from the British point of view. (*Basic Principles of Heating and Ventilation*, H. K. Lewis & Co., Ltd., London, 1948.) Readers will find in this volume a more extended treatment of the problems dealt with in this chapter.

southerly exposure tends to cut down insolation heat. Henry Niccols Wright has shown that in the vicinity of New York effective sun heat on a wall facing south is almost five times as great in winter as in summer, but on a wall facing west-north-west it is six times as great in summer as in winter (Figure

Vertical Walls of Various Orientation, Daily

Average Solar Radiation:

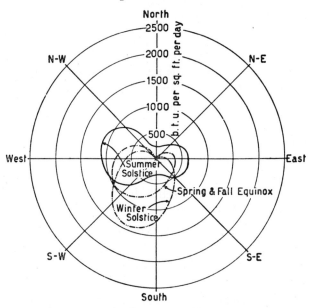

Figure 29. The average solar heat absorbed by vertical walls at various seasons in the latitude of New York. Solstices, June and December; equinoxes, March and September.

29). He changed the orientation of the same one-story house (in a laboratory model) from a position in which its principal rooms faced northwest to a position in which these rooms (with rearranged and slightly increased fenestration) faced west of south. This change decreased average summer sun heat to one-ninth and increased average winter sun heat to four times its value with the original orientation.

In summer the absorption of heat from insolation may be very considerable in amount. The influence of this factor varies with the intensity of solar radiation (as influenced by the transmission characteristics of the atmosphere), and by the angle of incidence of the sun's rays on a given building exposure. It also varies widely with the reflecting power of the exterior surfaces. Vernon[125] states that a dirty galvanized iron surface may absorb 91 per cent of the incident rays, while the same surface freshly whitewashed may absorb only 22 per cent. In the latitude of Detroit it was found that for a whole summer the glass windows of a certain building admitted only 17 B.T.U. per square foot per hour of sun heat; while when the sun was actually shining the figure rose to 150 B.T.U.

In planning for a given structure, there are of course many other factors than insolation to be considered. In designing a home, however, it would be generally advisable to arrange a long southern orientation for rooms designed for daytime occupancy. In a school, where both sides of the building are occupied in the daytime, it may be better to arrange the longer surfaces in a north-south direction so that all rooms receive some sunshine, rather than to produce ideal conditions on one side and poor conditions on the other.

In many locations prevailing winds may be of major importance. Protection from cold winds in winter and exposure to cooling breezes in summer, in such cases, may be more significant than relation to the sun. Furthermore, intelligent site-planning and relation to traffic arteries may have to be the determining factors.

All such problems must be taken into consideration and the most generally favorable compromise evolved.

Insulation

A second important factor which materially influences the solution of the problems of air conditioning is the degree of insulation provided in the construction of the building. It is costly to attempt to heat all outdoors, and the possibilities of economy and comfort may be materially increased by adequate insulation.

The importance of protection of this sort depends, of course, on climate. This factor is measured by the engineer in terms of "Degree Days" which are used as a basis for computing winter heating loads. For any one day there exist as many degree days as there are degrees Fahrenheit negative difference in temperature between the average outside temperature over a 24-hour period and a temperature of 65°F. Two thousand "degree-days" (for the winter season) represents a climate between that of Mobile and Birmingham; 4000 "degree-days" represents a climate that would be cooler than Nashville and warmer than Washington; 6000 "degree-days" would represent the climate of Providence and Cleveland; 8000 "degree-days" would be somewhat cooler than Milwaukee and warmer than Montreal.

This index is somewhat imperfect since it takes into account only air temperature and ignores the important factors of air movement and solar radiation. "Degree-days" provide a good measure of heating load in an office building in a closely built-up area; but they give a poor picture of what happens on an exposed hillside, facing heavy winds. A wind of 15 m.p.h. may increase the heat loss from a window surface by 47 per cent and from a concrete wall by 34 per cent.[46] Furthermore, absorption of moisture by a wall may greatly increase its conductivity.

Heat loss from a building includes three main factors, infiltration, transmission through walls and roof, and transmission through windows. Infiltration of cold air may vary enormously with tightness of construction; in well-built structures it is greatest around doors and windows. Heat loss through walls and roof may also vary widely. This factor is expressed in terms of heat transmission coefficients (representing the heat in B.T.U. transmitted in one hour per square foot of material for a difference of 1°F between inside and outside air). While a 1-inch thickness of concrete may transmit 12 B.T.U.

per hour per square foot per Fahrenheit degree difference in temperature, the corresponding value for felt or glass-wool insulation may be about one-quarter of a b.t.u. or only one-fiftieth as much. Furthermore, convection insulation such as this may often be profitably reenforced by radiation insulation. A layer of aluminum foil or some similar material which reflects radiant heat will add very greatly to the value of ordinary convection insulation in ceiling or walls. On the other hand, it is poor engineering to provide more insulation than is economically justified.

Rodee[111] has pointed out that the degree of insulation economically justified in a given case may be estimated by consideration of three factors: the demand made by the cooling influence of the winter climate of a particular area, the local cost of fuel, and the interest rate on the capital cost of the insulation to be provided. He presents graphs by which the relative importance of climatic heating load, cost of fuel, and cost of capital may be related; and, assuming an isolated building, 20 feet by 25 feet by 8 feet high, with approximately 100 square feet of window area, he computes heat losses for various structural methods and for different climatic conditions. Computations on the basis specified above indicate that an increased tightness of construction to eliminate direct convection (weather stripping and the like) which would cut air leakage from three to one-and-a-half changes per hour, would reduce heat loss from this source in millions of b.t.u. per year from 11 to 5 for the Mobile-Birmingham climate, and from 41 to 21 for the Milwaukee-Montreal climate. Double glazing would cut heat losses through windows from 6 to 2 millions of b.t.u. per year for the Mobile-Birmingham climate and from 22 to 9 for the Milwaukee-Montreal climate. So far as heat loss through walls and ceilings is concerned, it was found that decreasing the factor of heat transmission from 0.35 to 0.25 would reduce this type of heat loss from 23 to 16 for the Mobile-Birmingham climate and from 89 to 64 for the Milwaukee-Montreal climate. Reducing the coefficient to 0.05

would diminish the heat loss of this type to 3 and to 13 millions b.t.u. per year, for the respective climates.

The results of such theoretical computations may be materially modified in practice by the influence of heat capacity, radiant heat, earth temperature, and the necessity of maintaining an adequate number of air changes.

The use of materials such as aluminum or copper foil which have a high reflective value for heat rays is a distinct possibility of the future. Lorenzi, Herrington, and Winslow,[73] have shown that coating walls and ceiling of an experimental room with aluminum paper reduced the heating load by 21 per cent.

The problem of heat capacity, the power of a building material to accumulate heat, is another factor which may be taken into account by the architect of the future. It has been found in our laboratory[145] that in an experimental room, heated to 70°F in the daytime and allowed to cool down to 50°F at night, the period of night cooling effected a reduction in heating load of only 15 per cent in a brick structure of high heat capacity, as against 24 per cent in an identical frame structure of low heat capacity, on account of the large amount of heat necessary to warm up the brick wall when the heat was turned on.

A recent report by a group of visiting British engineers presents perhaps a better picture of the status of insulation in the United States than any similar brief review which we have seen in this country. Pritchard and his associates[105] note that the concept of providing special insulation in dwellings is more generally accepted in the United States than in England but is actually put into general practice only in the Northern sections of the country. Infiltration they find to be commonly, though by no means always, controlled by metal weather stripping. With regard to heat loss through windows they note that double glazing is particularly important in cold climates, not only for fuel saving but to decrease condensation and avoid discomfort from radiation to cold window surfaces and down drafts caused by such surfaces. They did not find double glazing to be general practice, except in Montreal. Roof insulation was much more prevalent than special insulation of walls, the insulation being generally placed above the top floor ceiling, not under the roof itself. In either case, "rigid" or "nonrigid" materials may be in competition with each other. Mineral wool, rock wool, glass wool, etc., are prominent in the second group.

Winter and Summer Air Conditioning in the Home

In the ordinary home (and the same condition holds with regard to small offices or other relatively small occupied spaces) there is no need to provide for special ventilation in the cold season, with the single exception that the moisture and the odors produced in cooking should be removed by a hood over the range. Protection is, of course, vitally essential in the case of any heating, cooking, or refrigeration appliances which may give off carbon monoxide or other toxic gases. In general no other objectionable gaseous materials need be anticipated in the atmosphere of the ordinary home. Odors from the bodies of occupants and from domestic sources will be adequately diluted by an air change of 10 cu. ft./min./person, and such a rate of air change will normally occur with building materials of ordinary porosity and doors and windows of ordinary construction in cold weather.

Märker and Schultze found that from four to eight cubic feet of air per hour may pass through 1 square yard of wall of sandstone, limestone, or brick with a temperature difference between inside and outside air of less than 10°F. With greater temperature differentials and a high wind the amount of air change may be much greater. British engineers have made many studies on this point by burning candles of known weight and computing the rate of increase in carbon dioxide which results. Vernon[125] cites rates varying from 0.16 to 0.77 air change per hour with no fireplace, and 0.9 to 5.0 air changes per hour with a fireplace opening. A rate of 1.5 air changes per hour is ample even with the minimum space allotment of 400 cubic feet per occupant, which is dictated by other hygienic requirements. If infiltration alone fails to meet this need, ventilation can readily be effected by opening of windows. On the whole no general plan for air-change, other than windows, is indicated for the normal home on the ground of dilution of atmospheric impurities. The introduction of new materials and construction methods which tend to make the dwelling really air-tight may alter this picture and may make it increasingly important to provide some means of controlled ventilation. In other words, the tighter the construction is made against heat loss, the more necessary it is to provide for air changes.

In general, however, the major objective of heating and ventilating in the home is to maintain physiologically adequate thermal conditions, to keep warm in winter and cool in summer.

The heating of indoor spaces generally involves both convective and radiative effects. There are, however, three general methods in use which may be classified according to the predominant influence of one or the other of these two types of heat:

A. Methods depending chiefly on convective heating.
   The "space heater,"
   The hot air furnace,
   The air conditioning system.
B. Methods involving both convective and radiative effects.
   The stove,
   The room radiator.
C. Methods depending chiefly on radiative heating.
   The open fire,
   The high temperature radiator,
   The panel heater.

Convective heating involves the warming of a given room by air which has been brought to a high temperature at some central point. Its simplest form is a "space heater," usually a jacketed stove, placed in one central room or a "pipeless furnace" immediately below the ground floor and discharging through a grating into a single room. Such a device as this is common practice in small homes, particularly in rural areas. It is, however, impossible with such a heater to secure desirably even distribution of heat, and the firing of the device and the removal of ashes create serious problems. The second type of convective heating—in which warm air from a cellar furnace (or a furnace in a special depression where no cellar is provided) is carried by pipes to each individual room—should be considered the lowest permissible standard for convective heating in new homes. Even this type is commonly subject to marked differentials in temperature, both horizontal and vertical (often showing gradients of 12° to 15°F). Care should therefore be taken in design and location of air inlets to avoid great local inequalities in temperature. A true air conditioning plant (supplying a larger volume of air at lower temperature) makes it easier to control distribution. This end is, however, accomplished by increased rates of air movement which require compensatory higher design temperatures; and the installation of such a system in the home is not justified except for a dwelling of a luxurious type.

A second type of heating combines convective and radiative heating effects by the location of heating units in each room. These may be stoves, which are subject to the same disadvantages noted with regard to space heaters. The two procedures are, of course, identical so far as the living room (in which the space heater is commonly located) is concerned. The stove is the simplest and cheapest form of heating for the very low cost dwelling and may be considered as a tolerable minimum, if present in every room. The Pritchard Report[105] gives an excellent picture of American practice with simpler forms of heating of this kind.

By far the most satisfactory form of heating by combined convective and radiative effects is the use of the room radiator through which steam or hot water circulates. Such systems of hot water or steam central heating are excellent for larger in-stallations. In an apartment project, fuel economics will go far to balance initial costs of installation, and more even distribu-tion and safety from fire hazards render the central heating plant the method of choice.

It is impossible at present to specify the particular type of radiator which is most economical and most hygienic, but a design which gives off a considerable proportion of its heat by radiation is desirable since it produces a maximum effect within the zone of occupancy, and a design which minimizes vertical differences in temperature is also helpful as decreasing the tendency to heat losses through the ceiling and upper side walls. The choice between steam and hot water systems, gravity and pressure systems, or one-pipe and two-pipe systems, free-standing or enclosed radiators, involves engineering technical-ities which we shall not discuss here.

Most "radiators" of the general type discussed above actually give off more than three-fourths of their heat to the air passing over their surfaces; in other words, they are really local units for convective heating. If we desire real radiative heating, we must turn to the third group of methods listed above. These, curiously enough, include the most primitive of all forms of house-heating, the open fire, and also the newest of all methods, panel heating. The open fire, of course, gives us only radiative heat, and since all its convective influence is dissi-pated up the chimney it is an economically wasteful process, although an adjunct to living which has great psychological attractions. The "hearth" and the "home" are traditionally synonymous.

More modern systems involving the use of radiative effects are of two distinct kinds. The first, known as High Tempera-ture Radiant Heating, involves the use of relatively small heating units at elevated temperatures (perhaps 1000°F). They are commonly gas heaters or electric heaters and are used in American homes as auxiliary heat sources, as in the case of the bathroom heater.

Panel heating, on the other hand, involves the warming of the room by large surfaces at a relatively low temperature (85° to 130°F). Under such a plan direct convection heating is reduced to a minimum, although the radiant heat from the warm surfaces is ultimately converted into convected heat after striking other cooler surfaces. There is a remarkable horizontal uniformity of air temperature throughout the room, and the floor-ceiling surface differential is comparable with that produced by free-standing radiators when ceiling panels are used and somewhat lower with floor heating. This system has been extensively used in England, most commonly in public buildings, with the heating units in rather high ceilings.

In American practice (particularly in factories and offices) the floor has often been used as a heating surface; and panels in the lower parts of the walls have also been employed with success. It seems possible to those who have studied these matters that certain types of panel heating may prove the pleasantest and most economical form of winter heating for residences. The system has three major potential advantages; architectural, in that it leaves the interior walls unmarred and the room space uncluttered; physiological, from uniformity of temperature and greater range for physical activity; and financial, in view of the claim that considerable fuel economies may be involved.

The present disadvantages are high first cost of installation and lag in performance, i.e. slow heating and slow cooling off. Both of these factors, however, depend on the type of panel heating used and not on the system in itself. Most installations in the United States have consisted of warm-water pipes embedded in a concrete floor or ceiling, and such a heating unit necessarily changes its temperature very slowly. Control by an outdoor-indoor thermostat will help to decrease the lag. It must be remembered, however, that there are many other ways of producing a large warm surface besides embedding pipes in concrete. Warm air may be introduced in a space above the ceiling or below the floor or inside the walls (as in the Roman hypocaust), and such a system is readily responsive to changes in temperature. Finally, where electric power costs are reasonable (as under the Tennessee Valley Authority), electrical power lends itself excellently to panel heating. In a panel-heated room the air temperature may be maintained at a level 2° to 3°F lower than would be necessary in a room with cooler walls.

The art of panel heating has come to us during the past ten years from England, and we owe to A. H. Barker, its original exponent, a real debt of gratitude. On the other hand the British observers, whose report has been several times cited above, point to the great advances made in this country in the development of warm-air furnace heating and central heating by steam and hot-water room radiators. They note that English fuel consumption is about four English tons per family per annum while American cities, with much more severe climatic conditions, only slightly exceed that figure (with an estimated consumption of 4.5 English tons), as a result of efficient design and operation of house heating appliances.

Under summer conditions, comfort can be practically promoted in three ways: by lowering air temperature, reducing humidity, or increasing air movement. Only in a very elaborate house will an air conditioning system be installed which can be used to cool and dehumidify air. It is possible, however, in dry climates to pass incoming air through a unit ventilator which permits the evaporation of water and thus lowers the air temperature. Some of the low-rent Federal Housing Authority dwellings in the Southwest are thus equipped.

Increase of comfort by air movement can be effected in two ways. The first of these is promotion of natural circulation by cross or through ventilation; and it is most important that orientation, room planning, and fenestration should make such natural ventilation possible. Windows should be so placed as to assure adequate circulation throughout each room, and their open area should extend close to the ceiling, within 6 inches if possible, to permit hot air in the upper part of the room to escape. Windows of the casement type which swing either horizontally or vertically are superior to the double-hung type since their entire area is made effective for ventilation. An additional advantage of the swinging type of sash is the possibility of controlling the direction of circulation by setting the angle of its panels. All double-hung windows should open at top and bottom. Adequate window area and careful placement of windows are especially important in kitchens, to remove heat resulting from cooking.

Exposure to prevailing summer winds is another major factor in securing comfort through high air movement during hot weather. Both warming in winter and cooling in summer are materially aided by suitable orientation of the dwelling toward the sun.

A second mode of utilizing air movement for summer cooling is the use of small electric fans within the room to create local drafts. A device which has yielded excellent results is the installation of an exhaust fan in the upper story to be turned on when the windows are opened in the evening to draw in the cool night air.

One important element in summer comfort is the heat capacity of the structure. High heat capacity may be undesirable under cold conditions, and for the sleeping room high heat capacity is probably undesirable even in summer. For the structure as a whole, however, high heat capacity in summer may offer desirable protection against extreme daytime heat, provided the nights are cool. This fact is mirrored in the adobe construction common in many warm climates with cool nights. In climates where nights as well as days are likely to be hot, high heat capacity walls will cause discomfort. In cold climates low heat capacity walls with high insulating value would obviously be desirable. Moreover, high heat capacity roofs tend to radiate their stored heat into bedrooms in the evening, so that insulation or other protection against this action is desirable.

Winter Air Conditioning in Schoolrooms and Similar Occupied Spaces

When we pass from the room in an ordinary dwelling to a space such as a schoolroom or a medium-sized office, occupied by from 30 to 50 persons, the nature of the problem changes. In such a space the occupants are crowded together, and some are very near the windows, others at considerable distance from them. Under such circumstances the use of windows alone cannot be relied upon to provide necessary air changes, even at the rate of 10 cubic feet per minute per occupant. Those seated near the windows will be too cold, or those seated near the interior wall will be too warm. Special provision for both ventilation and heating must be provided under these circumstances, the two objectives of heating and cooling being balanced against each other.

These considerations led quite naturally to the assumption that an elaborate system of mechanical forced ventilation was essential for the schoolroom, and in the early twentieth century many states passed laws requiring that all schoolrooms be provided with positive ventilation at the rate of 30 cubic feet per minute per person.

In 1923 the New York State Commission on Ventilation made an exhaustive study of this problem, on both a laboratory and a practical scale. Its field studies were primarily concerned with comparison of the then-standard procedure of fan-ventilation, supplying 30 cubic feet per minute per pupil, with a simpler system of window-gravity ventilation which admitted fresh outdoor air at the windows over slanting window boards and permitted the escape of warmed air by gravity ducts near the ceiling. The Sherman School at Fairfield, Connecticut, had been specially designed for the use of this system, and a number of schools in New York City were reconverted on the same plan.

The studies of the Committee demonstrated clearly that the simpler procedure was entirely satisfactory under most conditions and that the atmosphere of the window-ventilated rooms (with lower temperatures and less air movement) was generally preferred by observers to that of the fan-ventilated rooms.

When one realizes that the system of fan-ventilation is costly to install and to operate, this finding is of considerable importance. It was estimated that in an average year of school construction, the United States was spending at least three million dollars a year on this unnecessary luxury. In New York State alone it was estimated that $200,000 worth of fuel would be used in heating the extra 20 cubic feet of air per pupil to 70°F.[127] In actual practice it appeared that the elaborate systems of mechanical ventilation installed in compliance with the 30-cubic-foot law were very commonly not operated at all, and that when operated they were often so unintelligently managed as to produce objectionable rather than desirable results.[79] The American Society of Heating and Ventilating Engineers has abandoned the 30-cubic-foot standard, and its *Guide* now cites only 10 cubic feet of air change per person per minute as necessary with a cubic space allotment of 400 feet per person.

The changing viewpoint in regard to this problem has been strikingly illustrated in New York State. After a struggle extending over 20 years, the old 30-cubic-foot law was finally repealed and, instead of any inflexible requirement, the much wiser course was followed of delegating to the Commissioner of Education the power to approve the plans for any school building which "shall provide facilities for heating and ventilation adequate to maintain healthful and comfortable conditions in the classrooms and study halls." Under these broad powers, in November 1945 the Commissioner issued regulations with regard to the objectives of performance to be attained, and he will approve specific plans which he considers capable of meeting these objectives. The principle involved in such a method of control by performance standards (rather than by the specification of specific forms of apparatus) is so important that the Regulations may be cited in full.

167. *Heating and Ventilating.*

1. To obtain the approval of the Commissioner of Education of plans and specifications for heating and ventilating, there shall be compliance with the following requirements:

a. Thermal Environment During the Heating Season

(1) Heating systems shall be so designed and guaranteed that when properly installed and operated they will meet the following standards.

Type of Space	Design Operative Temperature[1]	Corresponding Room Air Temp.[2]
(a) Sedentary activity, as for example, in classrooms, auditoriums, offices, cafeterias...................	70°F	68°–72°F (30″ above floor)
(b) Moderate activity, as for example, in corridors, stairways, shops, laboratories, kitchens...............	68°	66°–70° (60″ above floor)
(c) Vigorous activity, as for example, in gymnasiums...	65°	60°–70° (60″ above floor)
(d) Special cases, lockers, and shower rooms..........	78°	76°–80° (60″ above floor)
Swimming pool area.......	83°	80°–86° (60″ above floor)

[1] The operative temperature represents the mean effect of the temperature of the air of a room and of its walls. Under normal conditions walls and air exert approximately equal effects; but if a room has three cold exterior walls a higher air temperature will be necessary for comfort than in the case of a room with a single exterior wall exposed to the sun but not to the prevailing winds.

[2] The lower figure of air temperature in each case is for a room with relatively warm walls; the second figure, for a room with relatively cold walls.

(2) Maximum air temperature gradient from floor to 60″ above floor shall not exceed 5° and preferably shall not exceed 3°.

(3) Air movement in zones of occupancy shall not exceed 25 linear feet per minute.

b. Thermal Environment During the Nonheating Season

(1) Where extensive summer use of rooms in a school building is anticipated in any area where outdoor summer temperatures are high, the Department may require the installation of air conditioning systems designed to produce inside temperature as indicated below

Outdoor Temperature	Indoor Temperature
80°F	75°F
90°	78°
95°	80°

(2) As an alternative to the above, the Department may require electric fans or similar apparatus which will increase turbulent air movement within such spaces as those specified above to 100 feet per minute.

c. Atmospheric Hazards and Quality

(1) In classrooms, provision for air change shall be made which, in the judgment of the Department, will provide a minimum air change of 10 cubic feet per minute per occupant. For effective thermal operation in mild weather a design factor of 15 c.f.m. is desirable.

(2) In rooms planned for close assembly a minimum air change of 10 c.f.m. per occupant shall be provided in order to remove odors. Additional air change, depending largely upon wall exposure, may be required for effective thermal operation in mild weather.

(3) In rooms where there is danger of toxic substances occurring in large concentrations, or where odors are likely to be strong, or where overheating is likely to occur, special ventilating equipment adequate to relieve the situation and entirely independent of the ventilating system serving the rest of the building, shall be installed.

d. There shall be furnished with the plans and specifications a brief, clear, and non-technical description of the heating and ventilating system together with instructions for operation.

With these regulations The Division of School Buildings and Grounds of the State Education Department issued a report of its consulting experts, which outlined five types of heating and ventilation "as procedures which may attain the desired results under various circumstances."

The first of these procedures is Direct Heating with Window Air Supply and Gravity Exhaust (the window-gravity system of the New York State Commission). It is described in the report of the experts[147] as "the simplest and commonly least expensive procedure available both as to installation and operation"; and "when installed with care and intelligence" as "capable of obtaining all essential results." This system involves three essential elements as follows: admission of fresh air at the windows, with upward deflection to avoid drafts (either over slanting window-boards or glass deflectors placed at the bottom of the window, or by narrow horizontal louvers under each window); tempering of this outdoor air and providing necessary heating by conventional room radiators installed beneath all the windows; and provision for the escape of heated air through gravity exhaust ducts located on the interior side of the room near the ceiling.

The second method, Direct Heating with Window Air Supply and Duct Exhaust with Central Fans, is the same as the first except that the exhaust is accelerated by fans. This procedure may be preferable in large buildings where the length of duct lines is considerable and where duct work is exposed to chilling in cold attics.

The third method is Direct Heating with Forced Unit Ventilator Air Supply and Corridor Gravity Exhaust. In this system air is introduced by unit ventilators placed usually at the windows, each with a small fan to introduce the required amount of air and a radiator to warm the incoming air to about 15°F below the desired room temperature. Additional conventional radiation must be provided to heat the room promptly in the morning and to carry the extra heating load in cold weather. The outward air flow is through grilles into the corridor and stair wells or through cowls on the top floor.

A fourth method is Forced Warm Air with Central or Zone Fans. This is the conventional system of mechanical ventilation (discussed more fully in a succeeding paragraph) in which radiation may be placed in the classroom to meet peak loads but where both heating and ventilation are primarily accomplished by a supply of warm air forced into each room through ducts by a plenum fan. As a rule the air inlet grilles are located near the ceiling on the inside wall, and outlet grilles near the floor on the same wall. This system is particularly adapted to large buildings in dusty, smoky, or noisy environments where the use of windows or unit air inlets is undesirable and where it is preferable to use a single plenum inlet equipped with washing or filtering devices. Overheating or drafts must be avoided by careful design and operation.

Finally, as a fifth possibility the report suggests Panel Heating with Window Air Supply and Duct Exhaust by Gravity or Central Fans. This is a modification of methods 1 and 2, in which the heating of the room is accomplished by low-temperature panel heating instead of high temperature local radiators, that is, by predominantly radiative effects and not by the combined radiative-convective heating of the conventional radiator. The New York State Commission report points out that "this type of system yields ideal thermal conditions, since it provides a more generally uniform temperature throughout the room at all levels."

Winter Air Conditioning of Larger and More Crowded Occupied Spaces

We have seen that in homes and other places where occupancy is low, both absolutely and in relation to space allotment, no special provision for ventilation is required. In the schoolroom we must make some special provision for air change, although the desired ends may often be accomplished by relatively simple methods, such as window-gravity ventilation. In assembly-rooms, auditoriums, large offices, and work shops—in general in all spaces occupied by 50 persons or more —ventilation cannot be accomplished without special mechanical appliances. In such spaces there is no satisfactory alternative to the plenum system of mechanical ventilation which consistently provides a supply of properly tempered air.

The fan used for operating such a system is generally of the axial flow or propeller type, in which the air is sucked in at the center of the fan and driven out in a direction parallel to the long diameter of the fan by a series of rapidly revolving blades. The radial flow or centrifugal type of fan has blades which operate in the open and drive the air at right angles to the plane of revolution of the fan. The centrifugal fan is often installed for exhaust ventilation over a range in a kitchen, for example, but it does not work well under pressure since a back current is often created, the air flowing in one direction at the periphery and in an opposite direction near the center of the fan. For forced duct ventilation the propeller type is therefore employed.

The central unit of the system may provide for heating the air only or for regulating relative humidity or for cleansing the air as well. If only temperatures are to be controlled, heating coils of desired capacity are placed in a chamber adjacent to the fan. For the removal of dust or soot the air may be passed through a filter or an air-washer. To deal with all these problems, an arrangement such as that shown in Figure 30 is commonly employed.

The fan, shown diagrammatically at the bottom, draws its air from the fan chamber and forces it out through the upper duct, the suction which it exerts producing a constant vacuum in the chamber, which draws in fresh air from outside through the filter at the right. In passing from this filter to the supply ducts, the incoming air is heated to a moderate degree (50° to 70°F, depending on various conditions) by passing through

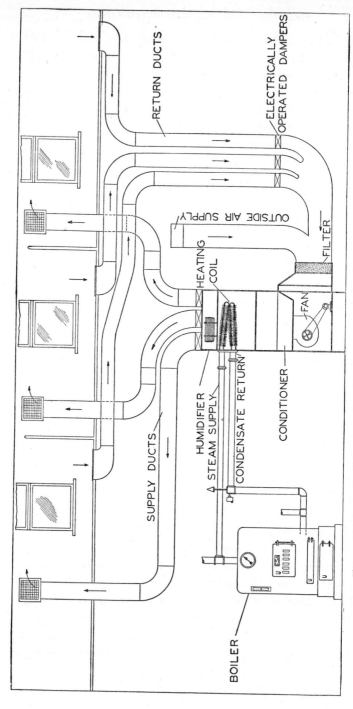

Figure 30. Generalized drawing of a plenum system of mechanical ventilation and heating of the type generally required where space occupancy is fifty or more persons.

tempering coils, which are lines of steam piping like those in an ordinary radiator, but so constructed as to present the largest possible surface to the rapidly moving air. After the tempering coils, the warmed air may be humidified by a steam jet. In many installations it passes through a spray chamber (not shown in Figure 30), filled with a fine mist of water produced by a spray discharge, and at its outlet end the air passes between a series of overlapping *eliminator plates* or baffles which change its direction suddenly many times. Contact with these baffle plates removes the excess of moisture which drains off from the eliminator to a collecting pan below.

Three things occur in a properly operating spray chamber. The air is humidified nearly to the point of saturation. It is cooled by the loss of the amount of heat required to transform the water taken up from the liquid to the gaseous form (5° to 10°F in summer time), and it is washed free from a portion of its suspended dust particles.

Finally, on leaving the spray chamber the air passes through a second set of heating coils (not shown in Fig. 30), where its temperature is brought up to the final point desired. The relation between the thermostatically controlled temperature at which the saturated air leaves the spray chamber and the temperature at which it leaves the final heating coils determines its relative humidity.

From the fan chamber the conditioned air is distributed to the various rooms in the building by suitably proportioned ducts, and the design of these ducts and of the dampers with which they are equipped is a complex problem, on the successful solution of which the final results achieved will largely depend.

The distribution of air within the rooms is another engineering problem of major importance. The linear velocity of air maintained in systems of fan ventilation will usually vary from 1200 to 2000 feet per minute in the main duct near the fan. As the air passes through horizontal branch ducts and vertical stacks its velocity is gradually reduced and at room inlets it is usually between 300 and 800 feet per minute. It is desirable that it should not exceed 300 feet per minute at such points in order to avoid unpleasant drafts. In order, therefore, to provide an air supply of 30 cubic feet per minute the inlet registers in any room should have a total area equal to 0.1 square foot per capita. Such an air supply as this is essential in large rooms, where relatively slight heat loss through exterior walls will take place and where each occupant is surrounded on all sides by other human bodies, so that no lateral radiative heat loss is possible. The average human being produces about 400 B.T.U. of heat per hour and one B.T.U. raises the temperature of 5 cubic feet of air by 10°F. Therefore, if we assume that 70°F is the desired air temperature and that 60°F is the lowest temperature of incoming air desirable to avoid local chilling, we shall need 2000 cubic feet of air per person per hour of air at 60°F to prevent the general room temperature from rising above 70°F. With no cooling by lateral wall radiation the Pettenkofer standard of 30 cubic feet per minute is valid on purely thermal grounds.

The problem of local drafts near the inlets may be greatly reduced by the use of inlet grilles of special design which diffuse the entering air laterally and mix it promptly with the general air of the room. It is also of great importance that the inlets and outlets be so placed as to secure reasonably even distribution throughout the room as a whole.

If, as is the case in a crowded auditorium, the chief objective of ventilation is to supply cool air to balance the heat produced by the metabolism of the occupants, an upward system of ventilation would seem logical, introducing cool air at or near the floor, this air being gradually warmed as it passes up to outlets near the ceiling. The warmth of the human body automatically induces an upcurrent which is in the neighborhood of 5 feet per minute, and it would seem natural to work with this upcurrent and not against it. This type of system is very commonly employed, with mushroom air diffusers under the seats reducing air velocity on the body to 25 feet per minute.

Even such an air current, directly on the ankles, may cause some discomfort, however, and the upward system also tends to carry up dust and dirt from the floor and feet of the occupants.

In installations where cost is not a paramount consideration, the theoretically unsound plan of downward ventilation has on the whole been found the most practically successful when provided with elaborate and carefully designed inlet diffusers for ceiling supply. This procedure has been used with notably satisfactory results in the Halls of the Senate and House of Representatives in Washington and in other large installations described by Vernon.[125]

For purposes of economy it is usual to recirculate a considerable portion of the air which passes out from the rooms through the outlet ducts back to, and through, the central air conditioning chamber. This procedure may reduce fuel costs by fifty per cent and is thoroughly sound practice, so long as enough fresh air is constantly added to prevent accumulation of undesirable odors.

Summer Air Conditioning

In the home, as pointed out above, the promotion of summer comfort is generally accomplished by increase of air movement alone. In the large and costly residence, and in other structures where financial limitations permit, it is possible to accomplish more far-reaching results by plenum supply of air which has been cooled or dehumidified. In warm climates such a process may be desirable for schools during the fall and spring. The process is commonly used in railroad trains in the United States in summer and in many luxury hotels, and in some department stores and offices. In industry the value of summer cooling is particularly great since, as pointed out in Chapter V, such a process may be directly related to productive efficiency. In tropical climates the importance of summer cooling becomes a major factor. In certain areas where our troops were stationed during the last war, the heat was so extreme that emotional breakdowns caused a serious drain on effectiveness; and it was found that night cooling of barracks greatly reduced such casualties. Throughout much of the southwestern part of the United States summer cooling is a far more important aspect of air conditioning than winter heating. In general, the future development of this aspect of the art is likely to be great. We have for centuries realized that man must be protected against winter cold but have assumed that summer heat was simply a dispensation of Divine Providence. This need no longer be the case, and summer-cooling may open vast possibilities in the development of tropical and subtropical regions.

The process of summer cooling is a complex one and cannot here be analyzed in detail. It is obvious that the type of air-conditioning plant described in earlier paragraphs and illustrated in Figure 30 can be applied to summer cooling by using (instead of steam condensed in ordinary heating coils) a refrigerant, such as certain methane compounds or ammonia, which is compressed to liquid form and then allowed to expand into a gas, absorbing heat from the air surrounding the pipes through which it flows and thus cooling that air. Sometimes the primary refrigerant does not cool the air directly but cools water or brine which, in turn, cools the air. Such a process ordinarily involves a double effect. It not only lowers the temperature of the air but—if the temperature reached is below the dew-point of that air—also dehumidifies it, which further improves the sensation of comfort. Additional dehumidification may also be obtained by passing the air through special sorbents (such as activated alumina, silica gel, or activated bauxite) which remove moisture by physical adsorption.

As pointed out in Chapter V, the indoor conditions to be maintained in summer should be warmer than those at which we aim in winter, on account of lighter clothing and physiological acclimatization. Too sharp a contrast between indoor and outdoor air must be avoided, since the chill experienced on entering a very cold building in summer and the shock experienced on passing from such a building to a hot street are both unpleasant and dangerous. It has been suggested that with an outdoor temperature of 95°F, indoor temperatures should not be below 80°F; while at 90°F outside, the differ-ential should be only 12°, and at 80°F outside, only 5°F. These are approximate estimates only, however, and the sub-ject requires more extensive study.

The Importance of Temperature Control

All mechanical systems of air conditioning are regulated by thermostats which are designed to control temperature and are sometimes combined with a hygroscopic element which con-trols humidity as well. When these devices are properly de-signed they are highly efficient and produce highly uniform results. Similar automatic regulation of this kind is available for the control of direct heating by radiators or panel heating, and even for heating by a warm-air furnace in the home. It is most desirable that such automatic regulation should be pro-vided for every occupied space, so far as possible, since persons exposed to an atmosphere which is too cold or too hot are frequently too preoccupied to notice the condition until con-siderable chilling or overheating has occurred.

In large buildings the problem of automatic regulation is complicated by local differences in exposure to sun and wind. To attain satisfactory results it is necessary to divide the duct system of air conditioning into separate zones, each with its own heating coils and circulating fan. Successful layout of such zones requires careful study of exposure to weather and of room use. It is often inadequate to zone simply by the wings or floors of the building.

While automatic temperature control should be standard practice in all heating systems, we believe that such control should ideally be supplemented by local hand control within a given room. The engineer and the plant operator dislike this procedure, which may create problems for them, but even the most perfect mechanical system may at times fail to meet special local conditions, and the occupant should have the option of obtaining more or less heat, of opening or closing a damper, or opening a window, whenever such an adjustment can be made possible.

Above all, we would urge the importance of the provision of room thermometers in homes, schools, offices, and factories. Such an instrument should be considered an essential part of the equipment of any occupied space; and in the school, factory, or office it should be the definite responsibility of someone to consult this instrument, which—unlike a thermostat—is effective only when connected with the humain brain. We have sometimes thought that it would be useful to invent a thermometer which would automatically liberate an odoriferous gas when the recorded temperature falls below or rises above predetermined limits. In any case, a more vivid realization of the fact that optimum thermal conditions are essential to human health, comfort, and efficiency must form an important part of planning for human welfare in the future.

CHAPTER VII

THE INFLUENCE OF CLIMATE
AND SEASON UPON HEALTH

Climate and Disease

THE influence of the thermal environment upon the human organism (as governed by metabolic activity, clothing, and other factors) must be similar indoors and out. Air conditioning is designed to produce an ideal interior climate, and outdoor climates which differ widely from the ideal cannot fail to exert an unfavorable influence in the outside world as well as in a home or factory.

The importance of climate as a factor in health was the central theme of the most famous treatises attributed to Hippocrates.[60] In *Airs, Waters, and Places,* he tells us that "whoever wishes to investigate medicine properly, should proceed thus; in the first place, consider the seasons of the year, and what effect each of them produces (for they are not all alike, but differ much from themselves in regard to their changes). Then, the winds, the hot and the cold, especially such as are common to all countries, and then such as are peculiar to each locality." Later, he says, "And, if it shall be thought that these things belong rather to meteorology, it will be admitted on second thought, that astronomy contributes not a little, but a very great deal indeed, to medicine. For, with the seasons, the digestive organs of men undergo a change." This treatise continued to be a fundamental text until a century-and-a-half ago.

In the eighteenth and early nineteenth centuries, the first

systematic studies of the actual relation of diseases to particular climates were made by Hoffmann (in 1746), Cortheusen (in 1771), Finke (in 1795), and Schnurren (in 1813). These volumes on "Medical Geography" have recently been reviewed by Barkhuus.[5] The most exhaustive work of this kind was published by August Hirsch in 1860.[61] World War II has recently led to the preparation of a monumental work on *Global Epidemiology,* under the editorship of General J. S. Simmons.[117]

Hirsch's monograph, which is the classic in this field, denies any influence of climate and season on influenza (although the figures cited show 85 epidemics beginning in winter and spring against 40 in summer and fall). Hirsch notes that smallpox deaths are at a maximum in February, March, and April. Measles, he recognizes as universal in its geographical distribution (except for areas where no importation of the disease had occurred), but as definitely associated in any climate with the cold season of the year. He makes the following acute observation on the factors involved in seasonal influence: "That this prevalence of the disease in the colder seasons is not in consequence of a change in the habits of living associated therewith—the crowding together in close rooms and the facilities thereby afforded for communicating the disease—may be inferred from the fact that the same degree of dependence on the season of the year obtains as much in the tropics as in high latitudes—in India, in Southern China, and in Brazil, countries where crowding in close rooms can hardly be taken into serious account as a factor in the etiology." In the case of scarlet fever, Hirsch's figures show little influence of either climate or season.

Passing to the intestinal diseases, cholera, of course, shows a peak in summer, with complex relationship to soil moisture, which Hirsch interprets in terms of Pettenkofer's ground water theory. Typhoid fever he considers as a disease of temperate rather than tropical climates, but in temperate climates its seasonal curve shows a very regular autumn peak.

Malaria normally occurs in serious proportions only in areas where the mean summer temperature exceeds 58°F; and shows a sharply marked seasonal incidence. Similar conclusions are drawn with regard to yellow fever, which Hirsch states has never become generally diffused in areas and at seasons where the temperature is below 68°F. Hirsch considers a moderately high temperature as most favorable to the development of plague epidemics, as contrasted with very cold or very hot conditions. Typhus fever, on the other hand, he recognizes as a disease of temperate and cold climates and of the winter season. The general accuracy of these observations (made nearly a century ago) is notable.

All of the reviews of this subject bring out two closely related phenomena. They indicate that a certain group of diseases (malaria, yellow fever, bubonic plague, typhoid fever, and cholera, for example) are prevalent in warm climates and at warm seasons, and that a second group of diseases (diphtheria, measles, scarlet fever, pneumonia, and typhus fever, for example) are prevalent in cold climates and at cold seasons.

In the case of communicable disease spread by insect vectors, we now understand clearly the nature of the phenomena involved. Malaria and yellow fever are warm weather diseases because the mosquitoes which serve as the agents for their transmission breed only at a high temperature.

Strong[120] points out that the limits of temperature and humidity for the *Glossina* which spreads African sleeping sickness are rather narrow and condition the epidemic occurrence of that disease, and notes that "extraordinarily slight changes . . . in the mutual adjustment profoundly alter clinical and epidemiological manifestations."

Bubonic plague is a warm weather disease, because the fleas which carry the germ of this infection from rat to man are abundant only at high temperatures. Robertson[108] points out that of 5 million cases of bubonic plague reported from all countries, except India, for a period of 26 years, 95 per cent occurred in areas where the mean midwinter temperature was over 50°F. With India included, the ratio rose to 99.8 per cent. Studies of the flea infestation of rats have shown that such infestation drops to a very low figure in cold weather. Pneumonic plague, on the other hand, is of course a disease of cold climates.

Excluding such infections as these, which are spread by insect vectors, there remain two major groups of diseases whose association with climate and season is less obvious. These are the maladies in which infection manifests itself in the intestinal tract (such as cholera, typhoid fever, dysentery, and summer diarrhea) which occur in warm climates and seasons, and those in which infection occurs by way of the upper respiratory tract (diphtheria, scarlet fever, colds, pneumonias, influenza) which are commonly epidemic in cold climates and seasons.

The graph for deaths from all causes in 1900 in Figure 25 of Chapter V shows the summer and winter peaks which were characteristic of mortality in temperate climates a half-century ago. Figure 31 is a reproduction of a cartoon which appeared in the Report of the Department of Health of the City of Chicago for 1907–1910, which does not too greatly exaggerate the problem.

That this variation with climate affects not only the more obvious respiratory infections but also rheumatic fever has been demonstrated by Nichol.[96]

Stern[119] points out that the spring is the season when exacerbations of various skin diseases occur with great frequency and attributes this phenomenon to the effect of increased sun radiation (which seems doubtful) and to dryness and high winds (which appear more probable factors).

The Studies of Ellsworth Huntington

Our knowledge of the relations of climatic conditions to human health and welfare were brought to a focus and made quantitative by the studies of Ellsworth Huntington, published thirty years ago.[65,66]

The technique employed by Huntington involved two de-

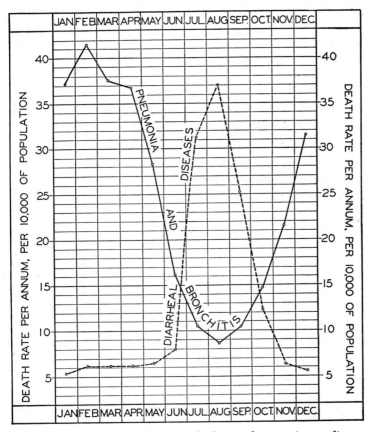

Figure 31. The seasonal change in death rates from respiratory diseases as contrasted with seasonal diarrheal death rates. (Report of the Department of Health, Chicago, 1907–1910, reproduced therein as a cartoon with the title "The Double Cross given Chicagoans by impure air and impure food diseases.")

vices, neither of them new, but novel in their simultaneous application to the problem in hand. In the first place he desired to use large masses of figures from various countries, particularly from countries where extreme climatic conditions obtained and where, in many instances, vital statistics were unreliable. To accomplish this end he took the monthly deaths actually reported in a given country for a series of years, plotted a trend line, and—for all subsequent analysis—used, not the actual deaths reported for a given month, but the difference between that number and the figure indicated on the general smoothed trend line. Thus, by dealing only with deviations from a trend line, he obtained a figure which was independent of the actual completeness of reporting and which would yield significant results, even if the completeness of reporting varied widely within the period studied, since such secular changes would influence the trend line but not the deviations therefrom.

Having thus obtained a figure for each month representing

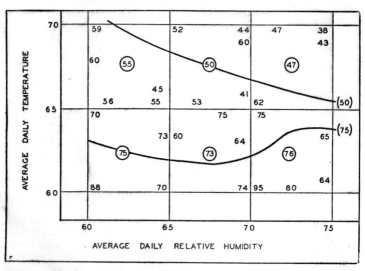

Figure 32. Contour chart in which pneumonia mortality deviations by months have been written in opposite the combination of temperature and humidity for a given month. Illustrates the Huntington climograph method of locating lines of constant mortality deviation in relation to temperature and humidity. (Reproduced from D. Greenberg, Relation of Meteorological Conditions to Pneumonia, *J. Am. Med. Assn.* 72, 252, 1919. By permission.)

the deviation of each month from the general trend line, Huntington prepared a graph, which he called a "climograph," in which the abscissa and ordinate represented two climatic variables. The ordinate generally represented the

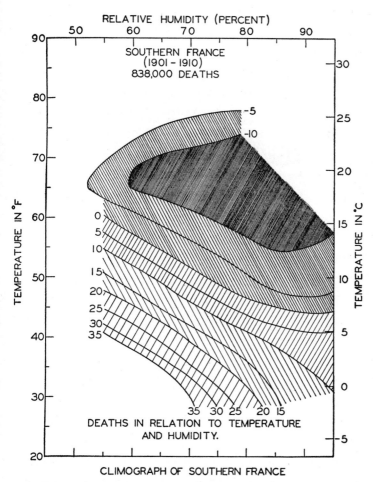

CLIMOGRAPH OF SOUTHERN FRANCE

Figure 33. Climograph showing percentage deviation (0 to +35, 0 to 10%) of death rate from its average value (indicated by curved isopract lines) in relation to temperature and humidity. Curved lines are obtained by plotting deviation of death rate for a given month in association with the temperature and humidity average for the month. (Reproduced from E. Huntington, *World Power and Evolution*, Yale University Press, 1919.)

231

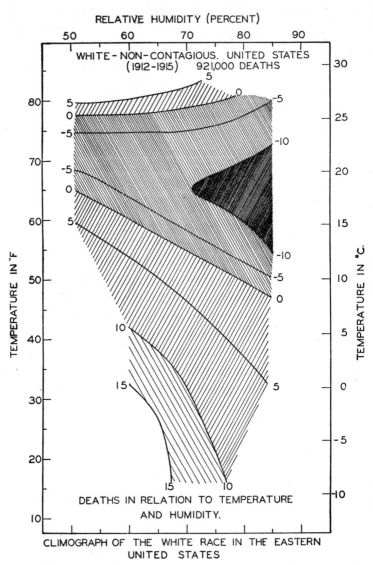

Figure 34. Climograph showing U. S. death rate deviations in relation to temperature and humidity (see legend of Figure 33). (Reproduced from E. Huntington, *World Power and Evolution*, Yale University Press, 1919.)

mean temperature of a month and the abscissa its mean relative humidity. Opposite the combination of temperature and humidity for a given month, he wrote in a figure representing the mortality-deviation recorded for that month. The process is illustrated in Figure 32 from a study by Greenberg.[42] Huntington then drew lines on the climograph representing the location of approximately constant deviations. Thus in Figure 32 it is obvious that most, though not all of the deviations above and to the right of the "50" line are under fifty, and that most of the deviations between the "50" line and the "75" line fall between the limits specified.

The smoothed climographs prepared in this fashion are published by Huntington in the general form indicated in Figures 33 and 34.

Figure 33 is the Huntington climograph for 838,000 deaths over a decade in Southern France, while Figure 34 is based on 921,000 deaths from noncontagious conditions in the United States in 1912–1915. In both cases, and in all the other climographs presented by Huntington, there is indication of increasing death rates above and below an optimum temperature and of increasing death rates below, and possibly above, an optimum relative humidity. The variously shaded areas indicate the combination of temperature and humidity for which data were available. It seems clear that for all the areas studied the months which showed a rate 10 per cent below the trend line were grouped in an essentially diamond shaped pattern and that the combination of 64°F temperature and 80 per cent relative humidity lies near the center of the diamond. Deviations in either direction from this central area are associated with increasing mortality, although data for very high humidity are generally lacking.

This technique has proved highly significant. Figures 35 and 36 are from the study of Greenberg cited above, which deals with specific types of diseases and not with the total death rate from all causes used by Huntington.

Figure 35 represents death rates from pneumonia in four American cities. It will be noted that here the relative influ-

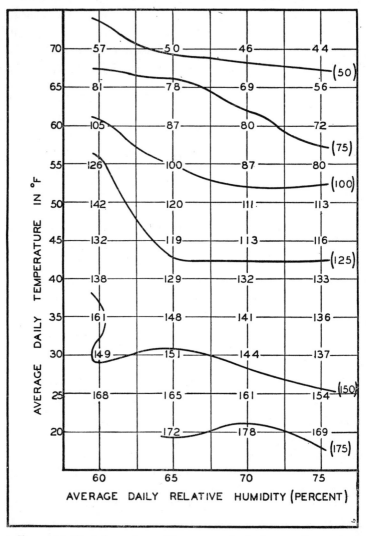

Figure 35. Deviations of monthly pneumonia death rates from annual mean (50 to 175% of annual mean) plotted in relation to mean daily temperature and humidity for given months. (D. Greenberg, *J. Am. Med. Assn.* 72, 252, 1919.)

ence of temperature is very great, the mortality in months with a mean temperature over 65°F being only 50 per cent of the general mean and that in months with a mean temperature of under 25°F, 75 per cent above the general mean. Relative humidity is also a real factor, as shown by a general slope of the lines downward to the right, signifying that low humidity is associated with higher mortality at a given temperature.

Figure 36 uses a different factor in the climograph, comparing mean monthly temperatures with the mean daily range of temperature for the month. Here it is clear that extreme changes in temperature are definitely unfavorable for pneumonia, since the climograph lines all slope downward to the left. A mean temperature of about 47°F with a mean daily

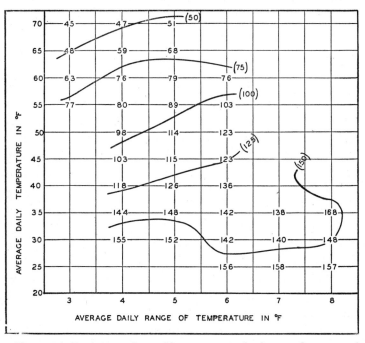

Figure 36. Deviations of monthly pneumonia death rates from annual mean (50 to 175% of annual mean) plotted in relation to mean daily temperature and mean daily range of temperature for given months. (D. Greenberg, *J. Am. Med. Assn.* 72, 252, 1919.)

range of less than 4°F is equivalent in effect to a mean temperature of 57°F with a mean daily range of over 6°F.

Such figures as these, for pneumonia, explain the increase in total death rates in the lower temperature ranges of Huntington's general climograph. Greenberg also studied seasonal variations in diarrhea and enteritis of children and found a large increase in total death rates at high atmospheric temperatures. The rates for these intestinal diseases are 50 per cent of the general mean at temperatures below 50°F, and over 200 per cent above the general mean at temperatures over 75°F. In the warmer ranges, high relative humidity is associated with increased mortality, 67°F with 80 per cent R.H. being equivalent to over 75°F with R.H. below 65 per cent.

The procedures and general conclusions of Huntington have been checked and confirmed, not only by Greenberg in the paper cited, but also by other investigators in the Department of Public Health at Yale University.

Margaret M. Justin[68] applied the Huntington techniques to mortality statistics for New York City, analyzing, separately, deaths from influenza and pneumonia, deaths of persons over 5 years of age, and deaths under 5 years of age. For the first and second of these groups, minimum mortality occurs at a mean temperature of 60° to 70°F and at a relative humidity of 60 to 70 per cent. For the group under 5 years (the infant diarrhea group) the optimum was at 55° to 60°F with a relative humidity of 60 to 70 per cent. Temperature was, of course, the more important factor, but pneumonia and influenza show an optimum (in cold weather only) at a relative humidity of 50 per cent, rising on either side of this optimum. This study, therefore, indicated a lower figure for relative humidity than that suggested by Huntington; and the New York data indicated no significant effects of variability.

Young,[151] using ordinary methods of statistical correlation, found a significant negative relationship between mortality from bronchitis and mean monthly temperature in London and in various Scotch cities during the winter months, with less striking correlations for pneumonia.

An unpublished Yale thesis by Greta Gray[41] dealt with statistics for Boston, Chicago, New York City, and the District of Columbia, and included eight separate groups of causes of death and a number of meteorological factors for each month of the year. In many months no significant correlation appeared; and for some meteorological conditions only one or two periods were studied, in others six such periods. The net results are indicated below in the proportion of total months analyzed, which showed significant correlations.

Statistically Significant Relations to Atmospheric Conditions
(Per Cent of Monthly Population Groups Studied
Showing Such Relations)

Cause of Death	Winter			Summer		
	Temp.	Hu-midity	Sun-shine	Temp.	Hu-midity	Sun-shine
All causes	−33	−10	0	+37	− 7	+ 3
Deaths under 1 yr.	−17	− 6	0	+39	−11	+33
Respiratory diseases	−22	− 3, + 3	0	− 5	0	0
Pulmonary tuberculosis	+ 8, −16	0	0	+ 8, − 8	− 8	+ 8
Brights disease, nephritis	− 8	+17	0	0	0	+17
Heart diseases	−17	− 8	0	0	−17	0
Diseases of nerv-ous system	− 8	+ 8	−8	+17	0	0
Cancer	0	0	0	0	0	0

Results for cancer are uniformly negative (as observed by Greenberg in the paper previously cited); and results for tuberculosis are highly variable, temperature showing occassional significant deviations of both negative and positive sign, both in winter and in summer. The other six groups of diseases all indicate a substantial proportion of negative correlations with temperature in winter, while all causes, deaths under one year, and diseases of the nervous system show a considerable proportion of positive correlations with temperature in summer.

Relative humidity does not yield many significant correlations, the only ones of considerable magnitude being a positive correlation with Bright's disease in winter and a negative correlation with heart disease in summer.

The amount of sunshine showed no significant relations in winter but had high positive correlation with deaths under one year and with Bright's disease in summer.

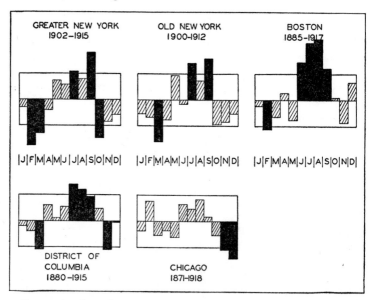

Figure 37. Plots of the correlation coefficients found for deaths from all causes. Plus coefficients are plotted above the baseline, negative coefficients below. The parallel lines on either side of the base line indicate the points to which the plots of the coefficients reach if the coefficients are three times their probable error. Example: In Greater New York increased September temperatures were associated with a significant excess in death rate. (Greta Gray, unpublished thesis, Department of Public Health, Yale University, 1926.)

The temperature data definitely confirm those of Huntington, as indicated in Figure 37.

Huntington's studies were not limited to mortality rates but extended also to various other measures of seasonal health and efficiency. Of special interest are data with regard to industrial production as registered by weekly earnings[65] in work places at various latitudes. Factory operatives in Connecticut showed a seasonal curve with a peak of efficiency in November and a rapid fall to a minimum in January to March. After this winter trough there was a steady rise, interrupted by a slight depression in July and August. The severe New England winter was definitely harmful but the moderate summer heat produced only a relatively slight effect. On the other hand, cigar workers in Florida showed maximum efficiency in December and January, and a sharp fall from June to August. The winter climate here was never severe enough to hamper production, but the hot summer had a marked effect. In the intermediate climates of South Carolina and Georgia, both winter and summer showed troughs in production but less marked than those for winter in Connecticut or for summer in Florida (Figure 38).

Mental work of students at Annapolis and West Point also showed peaks in fall and spring and troughs in winter and summer.

Huntington's general conclusion from all his studies is that human health is best and human energy highest at a mean 24-hour temperature of 64°F with a mean 24-hour relative humidity of 80 per cent. These mean values might, of course, be represented by a maximum temperature of 80°F in the daytime and a minimum temperature of 48°F at night, with similarly wide variations in relative humidity. Huntington also concludes that in addition to favorable mean temperature and mean relative humidity the most desirable climate is one which shows moderate variations in temperature from day to day, particularly falls in temperatures such as are associated with storms. The present authors do not find Huntington's

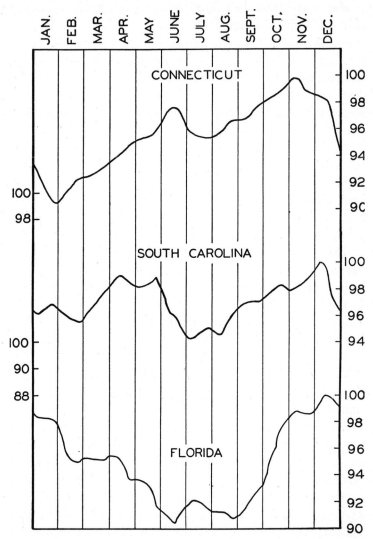

Figure 38. Seasonal variation of earnings (relative scale) of steadily employed factory operatives as a measure of "energy" in relation to climate. Illustrates winter depression in northern climate and summer depression in semi-tropical latitudes. (E. Huntington, *Civilization and Climate,* Yale University Press, 1913.)

evidence on this point as convincing as his data with regard to mean daily temperatures, and on this point we have not seen independent confirmatory evidence, but it is altogether reasonable to assume that a change from warm to cool might have a stimulating effect upon physiological processes.

On the basis of Huntington's conclusions that a mean winter temperature not below 38°F and a mean summer temperature not above 65°F is desirable, England, the northern Pacific Coast of the United States and Canada, New Zealand, parts of southern Chili and Patagonia have the most favorable temperature conditions. Patagonia is hampered by extreme dryness, however. Northwestern Europe and our own North Atlantic States have highly stimulating climates (from the standpoint of storminess) although their temperature range is extreme. Huntington has attempted to obtain a relative ranking of areas as to their general contribution to world culture, using a questionnaire addressed to a group of distinguished geographers and other authorities in various countries. He prepared comparative maps of "climatic energy" and "civilization" in the various parts of the world. In general, as would be expected, these experts give high rank to England and all of Northwestern Europe, and to the North Atlantic States and the Lake States and California in this country—all areas which have one or more of the conditions associated with ideal climate in considerable degree. Huntington fully realized that race stock and cultural heritage are also essential factors in a high civilization, but it is at least certain that a high degree of human efficiency has never been manifest in very cold or very hot climates or in areas such as many parts of Central Asia where extremes of both winter cold and summer heat prevail.*

* Interesting data were presented by Professor Huntington in his last book (*Mainsprings of Civilization*, John Wiley & Sons) indicating striking peaks of mental disease episodes, suicide, and sexual offenses in May and June. Although such findings may have no etiological significance, it seems probable that climatic effects may act as a precipitating stress in connection with such behavior.

Climatic Factors Influencing the Transmission
of Germ Diseases

Turning from these fascinating speculations to the problems of mortality and morbidity, where we have objective quantitative data to rely upon, there are several distinct ways in which climate and season may produce harmful effects.

The most obvious effect of the climatic environment upon health is to be found in its influence upon the arthropod vectors of disease. We have discussed this problem in an earlier paragraph.

In the case of the intestinal infections, such as typhoid, dysentery, and cholera, climatic variables of another type are at work. Such factors may be related both to the survival and multiplication of disease germs in the external environment and to seasonal variations in our own habits which influence opportunities for infection. The problem of survival of disease germs is a complex one. In a medium such as milk or food, in which pathogenic bacteria may actually multiply, high temperature favors such multiplication. The peak of summer diarrhea of infants in the days before pasteurization was an example of this phenomenon. In media where multiplication is not active, such as water, a diametrically opposite effect is manifest. Under such conditions, where anabolism is not possible, high temperatures accelerate katabolism, and pathogenic germs die out more rapidly as temperatures are increased. This is why, in the days when water-borne epidemics of typhoid fever were common, such epidemics occurred in fall and spring (at times of heavy rain washing pollution into lakes or reservoirs), and almost never in summer. It was possible at this time to tell by an examination of the seasonal typhoid curve of a city alone whether the public water supply played a major role in the dissemination of the disease. If it did, there would be triple peaks in spring, summer, and fall (Chicago); if it did not, there would be a single uniform curve with a summer peak alone (Boston, Figure 39).

A second factor influencing seasonal incidence of intestinal diseases is related to exposure as affected by our own habits of life. In summer we travel more and, especially in primitive vacation areas where sanitary precautions are likely to be sub-standard, we drink more water and consume more soft drinks, and we eat more fruits and other uncooked foods.

In the case of the respiratory diseases of winter there may also be influences of the season upon the process by which pathogenic germs may be distributed from one person to an-other. It is commonly assumed, particularly by those who emphasize the danger of atmospheric dissemination of infec-tion, that diseases of this type are prevalent in winter because of the crowding of human beings indoors at that season. Wells has made an interesting analysis of the seasonal patterns of measles and chicken-pox from this point of view.[149]

It should be noted that there is one disease, poliomyelitis, which displays seasonal characteristics apparently out of har-mony with the general contrast between summer intestinal infections and winter respiratory infections. This disease has

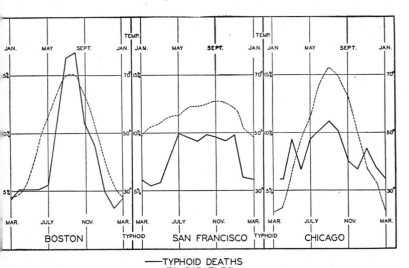

——— TYPHOID DEATHS
----- TEMPERATURE

Figure 39. Seasonal typhoid deaths, 1888-1897.[118]

243

at times prevailed in winter; but on the whole it shows a sharp peak of epidemic incidence in the early fall, a seasonal curve almost identical with that of typhoid fever. The epidemiological picture of poliomyelitis is, however, clearly that of a contact-born disease, normally and characteristically spread from one human being (generally a well carrier) to another. Its summer prevalence cannot be explained by influence of general environmental factors on the dissemination of germs since it is clear that human contact, and not food or water or insects, is the normal route of transfer. When it was thought that this disease was transmitted by discharges from the upper respiratory tract, the picture was a very puzzling one. Now that it has been demonstrated that the virus of poliomyelitis is more commonly prevalent in the alimentary discharges than in those of the nose and throat, a seasonal curve like that of contact-borne typhoid fever seems less anomalous.

Climatic Factors Influencing the Specific Resistance of the Human Organism to Infection

It is very difficult to see how the wider opportunities for dissemination of intestinal germs in summer and the increased possibilities of contact with respiratory germs in winter can fully explain the seasonal incidence of these types of infectious disease. The relation to atmospheric temperature is too close and too precise to be explicable on any such simple assumptions.

Consider, for example, the monthly variation in typhoid deaths, as analyzed nearly half a century ago.[113] The graphs in Figure 39 (with those from a number of other cities) were prepared by plotting mean monthly temperatures against typhoid mortality for the second succeeding month (allowing 2 weeks for incubation and 6 weeks to death). The curves for Boston and San Francisco are typical of the close relationship shown in cities which did not have polluted water supplies, and the third graph shows the completely different picture observed where spring and fall water epidemics were superimposed on the normal seasonal curve of contact typhoid. It seems quite impossible to assume that such perfect parallelism could result solely, or even primarily, from increased opportunities for transmission in summer.

With regard to the respiratory diseases, Gover, Reed and Collins[44] found that while no significant differences were manifest in the comparative incidence of respiratory infections in six American cities with highly diverse climates, within a given city weekly deviations from the norm of the respiratory attack rate showed a small but significant negative correlation with deviations from the norm of mean weekly daily temperatures. As might be expected this association was higher in the fall months. Even more striking results were obtained in a study of absenteeism due to respiratory illness conducted by the New York State Commission on Ventilation in Schools of Cattaraugus County, New York.[20] The figures below can scarcely be explained by any considerable relation to weekly variations in those factors which influence the spread of germs from pupil to pupil during the school season.

Correlation Between Weekly Respiratory Illness Rates and Mean Weekly Temperature Expressed as 70°F minus Mean Outdoor Temperature.

1926–27	+0.42	±0.11
1927–28	+0.55	±0.13
1928–29	+0.66	±0.12

It should be noted that such a close relationship cannot be expected in a large city, where the occurrence of extensive widespread epidemics during one or two particular weeks will frequently mask any effects relating to season alone. The demonstration was possible in Cattaraugus County because we were dealing with a large number of small rural schools in scattered and more or less isolated populations.

One other bit of evidence bearing on this point is the observation, frequently made in the days when infant diarrhea was a common disease, that sharp increases in temperature for a single week were accompanied by a corresponding sudden rise in infant mortality.

The most convincing evidence in this field, however, is to be found in the natural history of diphtheria and scarlet fever in tropical areas. In these two diseases we can compare the incidence of clinical disease in a population with the presence of nonclinical infection, as indicated by Schick and Dick tests.

Doull [25] made an important contribution to this subject by showing that diphtheria and scarlet fever occur at younger age periods in tropical and subtropical regions than in colder climates. He attributes this fact to earlier and more widespread immunity in warm climates due to a higher prevalence of subclinical infections. This is what we should expect if the distribution of germs were the same, but only if the high temperature tended to limit the degree of clinical infection through its direct physiological effects. This suggestion was confirmed on the other side of the globe by Parr, Goodale, and Kirschner,[101] who showed that in the Syrian States under French mandate, while clinical cases of scarlet fever and diphtheria were very rare in that warm country, acquired immunity due to subclinical infection was very high. The authors cite similar observations by other observers from Brazil, the Philippines, the Malay States, Honduras, India, and Palestine. This type of evidence seems to prove conclusively that the influence of warm climates and, by inference, of warm seasons, is not due to lessened spread of germs by lack of crowding together of human individuals but to an effect of warmth on the extent of large-scale invasion of the body tissues from their external surfaces. Clearly such phenomena as those discussed must be related primarily to the influence of temperature upon the ability of the human organism to resist infection. Charles E. North, in a communication[98] which has never received the attention it deserves, suggested a simple and plausible underlying physiological basis for such a phenomenon. North's thesis was that in a cold atmosphere the superficial blood vessels of the skin and of the oral and nasal mucosa are constricted, and the latter surfaces are thus depleted in their blood supply and therefore less effectively protected against invasion by germs which enter through the respiratory route. In a hot atmosphere the situation is reversed. Under such conditions the vessels of the skin and the mucosa are expanded at the cost of constriction of the blood vessels of the intestinal mucosa, a condition which favors invasion by germs which infect by that route.

This explanation seems too simple to be all-embracing, but that the phenomenon must occur seems obvious. Some such fundamental physiological concept would seem essential to the explanation of the remarkable relationship of the two types of disease mentioned to the two extremes of climate.

How such a physiological mechanism may operate has been pointed out in our review of the work of Mudd and his associates in Chapter III.[88, 89] Another interesting suggestion has come from Nungester and Klepsen,[99] who reported a series of experiments in which the introduction of pneumococci into the noses of rats produced an infection rate of 13 per cent with control animals and of 38 to 42 per cent with animals exposed to cold, to alcoholic intoxication, or deep ether anesthesia. The authors concluded that one factor in the higher infection rate was alteration in the normal functioning of the epiglottis and vocal folds. They observed that when a stimulus was applied to the posterior pharyngeal region the epiglottis and vocal folds failed to close the trachea in 18 per cent of control animals and in 46 to 54 per cent of the animals exposed to chilling or alcohol.

With respect to the intestinal conditions, Goldwasser and Kligler[40] offer suggestive observations on the influence of seasons on the intestinal flora of normal human beings in Palestine, which they summarize as follows: "During the winter a condition of equilibrium exists, the number of bacteria is relatively high, the moisture content is low, and cocci and anaerobic spore-formers predominate. In the spring (about April or May) there is a transformation: the total number of bacteria falls, the coli preponderate, and cocci and anaerobic spore-formers diminish. The curve of the coli-cocci ratio follows closely that of bacillary dysentery, suggesting some relation to the same primary favorable factors, the change in the intestinal environment favoring the development of this group of bacteria."

All in all, it seems reasonable to assume that the susceptibility to intestinal disease in warm climates and seasons, and to respiratory diseases in cold climates and seasons, is largely due to differences in resistance to invasion of the mucosal surfaces concerned, caused by fluctuations in relative distribution of blood supply arising from direct physiological adaptation to environmental temperatures.

Climatic Factors Influencing the General Vital Resistance of the Human Body

We have discussed two sets of climatic influences—those favoring the general transmission of infectious agents from person to person, and those affecting the readiness with which such agents actually penetrate the barriers of the oral and the intestinal mucosa. The thermal factors of our environment, however, also exert profound effects on the resistance of the body to the actual disease process after it is initiated, and on the physiological status of the body itself, quite apart from any infectious process whatsoever. The obvious extremes of such effects are heat stroke on the one hand and death by freezing on the other. The influences of climate and season upon morbidity and mortality from a given disease are quite independent of each other. Thus typhoid morbidity, as we have seen, is highest in the fall months, but fatality rates from this disease (ratios of deaths to cases) are highest in the cold months.[126]

Gover[43] reports that deaths from all causes in 86 cities in the United States during the summer months showed a significant positive correlation between weekly deviations from normal mortality rates and deviations from normal mean maximum temperatures (for the preceding week). This increase manifested itself chiefly in diseases of the heart, arteries, and kidneys, and penumonia, so that it mirrors an influence on general physiological status and not on incidence of intestinal diseases.

An exceedingly hot week (July 21–28) in 1934 was accompanied by enormous rises in mortality in certain Middle Western States.[21] For the 86 large cities of the country as a whole, the mortality rose to 12.3 per 1000 as compared with an expected rate of 10.6. In the 8 cities in the particular area most affected (Chicago, Cincinnati, Columbus, Des Moines, Indianapolis, Kansas City, Omaha, and St. Louis) the rate for this week was 25.5 per 1000, as compared with an expectation of 12.4.

The ways in which climate and season influence physiological processes may, of course, be diverse. Hess and Unger[57] called attention to the fact that the seasonal prevalence of rickets (reaching its peak in March) was paralleled by a decrease in the inorganic phosphate content of the blood, a general seasonal wave of physiological status. Whether the low phosphate content tends to cause an increase in rickets or the prevalence of rickets lowers phosphate content is uncertain. Nor can we yet determine whether the effect of climate upon either the physiological chemistry of the body or upon the prevalence of nutritional disease is a direct reaction to temperature or to sunlight or to some other environmental factor which, in turn, is influenced by temperature or sunlight. Goldberger, Wheeler, and Sydenstricker[39] have pointed out that the spring peak of pellagra is related to seasonal variations in the food supply of Southern mill-village populations.

Aycock,[3] in a study on possible contributory factors in the prevalence of poliomyelitis, has presented an exceedingly suggestive review of cyclical changes in various physiological characteristics. He cites seasonal variations in the organ weights of rabbits (Brown, Pearce, and Van Allen) in which the testicles and thyroid show a spring maximum and the parathyroid and popliteal glands a fall minimum; variations in the weight gain of children at different seasons, as recorded by various observers, with a maximum in late summer and fall (in Porter's observations, the rate of gain during the last five months of the year being more than four times that for the first five months of the year); variations in the iodine content of the thyroid gland in cattle, sheep, and hogs (Seidell and Fenger) in which the iodine content from June to November was three times that for December to May; variations in the resistance of guinea pigs to diphtheria toxin, with higher survival values in summer than in winter (Sudmersen and Glenny); variations in susceptibility of mice to acetonitrile poisoning (Hunt), with greater resistance in winter than in summer.

Strong[120] states that "individuals are rendered more susceptible to a number of diseases by chilling and cold, and bronchial and other respiratory and lung affections, as pneumonia, are more common in winter than in summer. On the other hand, a tropical, moist, monotonous climate may weaken resistance against infections, not because it disturbs metabolism, as has been emphasized by some, but on account of its failure to stimulate sufficiently the thyroid, adrenal apparatus and the sympathetic system."

The whole field is a complex one and the results diverse, as would be expected from the fact that "resistances" to various conditions must be specifically related to particular chemical variations in the body, and these relations, in turn, governed by various dietary factors and by the activity of various endocrine organs. That the human body does exhibit marked seasonal cycles in its specific physiological functions is, however, clear; and this subject of seasonal cycles is one which, in recent preoccupation with the microbic factors in disease, has received far less attention from epidemiologists than it deserves.

At least the following conclusions seem apparent from the evidence in hand:

1. Extreme heat or cold lead directly to fatal results, and even such temperature variations as occur in the United States may increase general mortality rates to double their normal volume (as demonstrated in the "hot week" of 1934).

2. Minimum mortality rates occur with a daily mean temperature of 60° to 70°F and with a mean daily relative humidity of 60 to 80 per cent (at a figure perhaps lower than the 80 per cent of Huntington).

3. Industrial production and intellectual and social achievement are also highest in climates and at seasons where such conditions as those cited above prevail. The general level of such achievement appears to be definitely favored by the stimulus of moderate (but not extreme) variations toward the colder side of the optimum range.

4. The human body displays regular annual rhythms of physiological activity as displayed by variations in blood chemistry, in endocrine activity, and in resistance to poison and to disease, which are little understood but which are perhaps related to the late winter peak of mortality.

5. Seasonal and climatic variations in morbidity from the communicable diseases are particularly significant, and always tend to show an increase in intestinal infections under hot conditions, and an increase in respiratory infections under cold conditions. This correlation can be explained only in part by influences affecting the facility with which the infectious agents are disseminated through a community. It is so close and so general that it can be understood only on the assumption that direct physiological responses to temperature govern the power of the nasal and oral mucosa and the intestinal mucosa, respectively, to resist invasion. This conclusion is clinched by the fact that in diphtheria and scarlet fever we have clear evidence that in the tropics distribution of the germs (as demonstrated by acquired immunity) is as general as in northern climates, while actual clinical manifestations are relatively rare. The decreased blood supply of the nasal and oral mucosa under cold conditions, and the decreased blood

supply of the intestinal mucosa under warm conditions, would seem to be an important factor influencing such variations in resistance to invasion.

The Alleged Influence of Climatic Overstimulation

An interesting new hypothesis was proposed by Mills[82-87] in a series of papers attributing higher rates of mortality from diabetes, exophthalmic goiter, pernicious anemia, and Addison's disease in the northern United States to a greater intensity of what he called "climatic drive." He accepted Huntington's thesis of the general stimulating influence of a cold climate but suggested that greater intensity of activity was obtained at a physiological cost, registered in increased mortality from what he considered "metabolic diseases." This theory was, in part, based on comparison with the effect of extreme heat and cold upon experimental laboratory animals (Ogle and Mills), a doubtful analogy, since these animals depend largely on processes of chemical heat regulation, not important to man; and his statistical studies did not give recognition to factors other than geographical location. Nevertheless, the suggestion seemed sufficiently interesting and plausible to warrant study by other methods. Moriyama and one of us, therefore, explored the actual situation in greater detail.

In the first of our studies[55] we analyzed the data for the five diseases stressed by Mills for each of the 44 States in the Registration Area for a 10-year period, comparing age-adjusted mortality rates with 11 climatic factors and 11 socio-economic factors. There was a generally high correlation between variation in the 5 different diseases and a general pattern of relationship between the 5 individual causes of death and most of the climatic and socio-economic variables, and between the climatic and socio-economic factors themselves. Thus, for example, mean temperature showed a negative correlation of 0.52 to 0.69 with income, with residence telephones, and with value of products. Clearly, geographical correlations by themselves are meaningless, since high economic status might naturally be expected to influence a disease like diabetes, associated with ample diet, and diseases like Addison's disease, leukemia, and pernicious anemia, whose recognition depends so much on high-quality medical diagnosis.

Analysis of partial correlations showed, in fact, that the socio-economic factors are far more important than the climatic factors in relation to mortality from diabetes. A residual significant relationship, in which diabetes is associated with lower normal temperatures and increased wind movement may most reasonably be explained by the cardio-vascular complications and intercurrent respiratory infections to which the diabetic is exposed, since, according to prevailing practice in the certification of combined causes of death, deaths from such causes in a diabetic are allocated to diabetes. There seems no reason to conclude that any harmful effect of "climatic drive" upon metabolic processes is involved.

Similarly, in the case of exophthalmic goiter, pernicious anemia, and leukemia, the socio-economic factors showed much greater statistical influence than the climatic factors, only Addison's disease registering higher negative correlations with temperature than with other factors.

In a second contribution[81] the influences of climatic and socio-economic factors upon diseases of the cardio-vascular and renal systems were similarly analyzed. In the case of diseases of the circulatory system, cerebral hemorrhage, and chronic nephritis, socio-economic factors were far more important than climatic factors in a proportion of 3 to 1 for the first and third groups of diseases, and of 30 to 1 for cerebral hemorrhage. Only in the case of angina pectoris (where a direct effect of the shock of chilling is obvious) were climatic factors of determining importance.

In general the authors conclude that the results presented in these two papers "throw serious doubt on the conclusion of

Mills that 'a whipping up of the activity of the glands of internal secretion . . . seems to answer the question as to how weather fluctuation affects the human body.'

"We have shown that the climatic conditions which are supposed to increase mortality from metabolic diseases are closely associated with a 'concealed classification' of socio-economic factors which are of major significance. In the case of such metabolic diseases as diabetes, pernicious anemia, exophthalmic goiter, and leukemia, these socio-economic factors account for two-thirds to four-fifths of the observed geographical differences and the same ratio holds for such cardiovascular and renal conditions as the circulatory diseases, cerebral hemorrhage and chronic nephritis. Only Addison's disease in the first group, and angina pectoris in the second, are more closely correlated with climatic than with socio-economic factors.

"It seems to us that the relatively small fraction of the total geographical variation associated with climate can, in large measure, be explained by the direct influence of severe winter climates on the circulatory system and the association of such climates with high incidence of intercurrent respiratory infections rather than by assumption of a direct deleterious influence of climate upon the activity of the glandular system; particularly in the human organism whose metabolism is not markedly influenced by atmospheric temperatures.

"Finally, the climatic factors found by a competent statistical analysis to be actually associated with mortality are related to a cold and damp climate rather than to a stormy, variable one. Of thirteen significant, predictive, climatic factors, noted in this and our preceding paper, which might be considered representative of storminess and variability (cyclones, anticyclones, and temperature variability), eight are actually associated with *low* mortality. Of eleven such factors, representative merely of cold or dampness, ten are associated with high mortality."

Thus, considering all the evidence at hand, we can only

predicate with certainty that extremes of heat and cold are definitely harmful; and that even moderately hot conditions increase susceptibility to intestinal diseases, and moderately cold conditions increase susceptibility to respiratory diseases. These are simple conclusions but they are of far-reaching significance, both from an epidemiological and from a physiological standpoint.

The Man-made Climate of Interior Spaces

Clothing will materially help in an adjustment to an unfavorable outdoor atmospheric environment, but for more far-reaching results we must look to the creation of artificial climates by the air conditioning of houses and schools and work places.

Markham[75] has pointed out that on a world map of annual mean temperatures the isotherm of 70°F passes through or close to all the centers of early civilization in Egypt, Palestine, Assyria, Sumeria, and Persia, and not far north of Mohenjodara, the cradle of culture in the Valley of the Indus. He believes that when the mean temperature of the hottest month of the year exceeds 75°F, the white immigrant and his children may be able to tolerate the changed conditions, but that his grandchildren will show a definite loss of energy and of mental and physical efficiency.

Brunt[15] makes the acute observation that the invention of the hypocaust made it possible for civilization to spread northward, and provided a basis for the great days of Athens (annual mean temperature, 63°F) and of Rome (annual mean temperature, 60°F). "With the fall of the Roman Empire," he says, "indoor heating became far less common and almost died away, and the next major civilization, the Moslem, was again in the region of the 70°F isotherm. Later on, in Western Europe, as indoor heating developed and houses once again became weatherproof, civilization began to make rapid strides." It was not until the time of Henry VIII that tight construction of dwellings, glazing of windows, and construction of efficient

255

fireplaces and chimneys became available in England, even for the wealthy, and not till the sixteenth century that such facilities became widespread. Brunt adds, "Once weatherproofing houses had become general, England had a great advantage in its cheap supply of coal for indoor heating, and it may not be a fortuitous coincidence that the glories of Elizabethan England came soon after the advent of the weatherproofed house."

So much for the possible far-reaching effects of indoor heating in winter. This has, so far, been the only type of air conditioning in universal use. Today, however, we can cool in summer as well as we can heat in winter. The powerful and efficient nations of the past century have been those of Northwestern Europe and Northern North America, where mean monthly summer temperatures of over 75°F are rare and where winter conditions have been controlled by indoor heating. May not vast areas in the sub-tropics become the seat of mighty civilizations, as summer air conditioning meets human physiological needs with similar efficiency?

GLOSSARY

Calorie In the present book, this is the "large calorie"; the amount of heat energy required to raise the temperature of one kilogram of water 1°C.

ΔH Heat Change. Change in mean temperature of body tissues in a given time multiplied by body weight and the specific heat of the body (called "Storage" in an earlier paper, with a reversed sign). Expressed in calories per square meter of body surface or in calories per individual.

E Evaporation. The amount of heat loss due to evaporation from skin and oral surfaces in a given time (expressed in calories per square meter of body surface or in calories per individual).

E.T. Effective Temperature. The temperature of air with 100% relative humidity and minimal air movement which would exert the same influence upon heat sensation as any given combination of air temperature, air movement, and relative humidity (determined experimentally by records of comfort votes in studies made by the American Society of Heating and Ventilating Engineers).

I_A Insulation of the Air. An expression in resistance units, similar to I_{cl}, of the insulating value of air under the environmental conditions connected with the definition of the clo value.

I_{cl}. Clo. The insulating value in resistance units (reciprocal of conductance expressions) of a clothing assembly which will provide heat balance for a heat production of one met at an air temperature of 70°F with minimal air movement and relative humidity of 50%.

K Conductance. Heat flow through the skin per unit difference between skin temperature and body temperature

$$\frac{M \pm \Delta H}{A} \div T_B - T_S$$

where M = metabolism; ΔH = change in temperature of body tissues multiplied by body weight in kilograms and specific heat of body tissues, 0.83 per kilogram; A = surface area of body in square meters; T_B = rectal temperature; T_S = skin temperature ($^\circ$C).

K_C Convection Constant. The experimentally determined heat flux per degree temperature difference between mean body surface temperature and air temperature; expressed in calories per square meter per hour or per individual.

K_R Radiation Constant. The experimentally determined heat flux per degree temperature difference between mean body surface temperature and air temperature; expressed in calories per square meter per hour or per individual.

M Metabolism. Heat produced in the human body through the combustion of food; expressed as calories per square meter of body surface or per individual.

Met   A standard rate of metabolism, 50 calories per square meter per hour, typical of seated subjects at rest under non-fasting conditions.

Partitional Calorimetry. The process of analyzing heat interchanges between the body and its environment in such a way as to determine the simultaneous influences of convection, evaporation, and radiation in relation to metabolism and heat change.

R Radiation. Heat exchange between the body and its environment due to radiative interchanges with surrounding surfaces (expressed in calories per square meter of body surface or per individual).

Surface Area. An expression in square meters of the total skin surface of the body when used in connection with units of metabolism, or units of convection loss. When radiation exchange is involved, a reduced area (70–80 per cent) representing the integrated profile area of the body.

T_A Air Temperature, determined by thermometers or thermocouples shielded from radiation effects from walls or other objects at temperatures above or below air temperature.

T_{Cl} Mean temperature of clothing surface and exposed skin areas, determined in a manner analogous to that used for T_S.

T_O Operative temperature. Temperature representing the combined effect of an environment exerting various influences upon heat interchange by convection and radiation, weighted to take account of air temperature and mean radiant temperature. (If air and walls are at the same temperature, T_o = air temperature.)

T_R Rectal Temperature, determined by means of thermocouple left in place during an experimental period.

T_r Temperature of radiating surfaces of the body in the calculation of Brunt (Chap. III).

T_s Mean Skin Temperature. The average of 15 local skin temperature fields weighted according to the percentages of skin surface in the four principal body segments; Head, Trunk, Upper, and Lower Extremities.

T_W Temperature of Wall Surfaces. The radiant temperature of surrounding surfaces as determined by thermopile or thermocouple methods.

W Work. The fraction of the metabolism which is dissipated during exercise in the form of energy transferred to the environment (ergometer motion). Expressed here in heat units comparable to those used for metabolism. To be distinguished from W in the compound symbol $W\mu$, and from abbreviations of weight.

μ Constant of Evaporative Exchange. This evaporative cooling constant is expressed in calories per square meter of body surface per hour per centimeter vapor difference (Hg units) between skin surface and ambient air.

$W\mu$ Wetted Area. A physiological variable which describes the extent of moisture present on the skin surfaces of the body ($W\mu$ = per cent of total surface wet).

V Air Velocity. Average air movement in feet per minute or centimeters per second, as determined by a hot wire anemometer.

Temperature Conversion Table

$$°C = (°F - 32)\tfrac{5}{9}$$

°C	°F	°C	°F
0	32.0	30	86.0
5	41.0	35	95.0
10	50.0	40	104.0
15	59.0	45	113.0
20	68.0	50	122.0
25	77.0		

REFERENCES

1. Aldrich, L. B. 1928. Smithsonian Miscellaneous Collection, 81, No. 6.
2. American Society of Heating and Ventilating Engineers. *A.S.H.V.E. Guide,* 1948 (published annually).
3. Aycock, W. L. 1929. *Jour. Prev. Med., 3,* 245.
4. Azzi, A. 1921, *La Riforma Medica., 37,* 509.
5. Barkhuus, A. 1945. *Ciba Symposium, 6,* 1997.
6. Bartley, S. H., and Chute, E. 1947. *Fatigue and Impairment in Man.* McGraw-Hill Book Company, New York.
7. Bazett, H. C. *Physiology of Human Heat Regulation.* (Edited by L. H. Newburgh.) W. B. Saunders, Philadelphia, Pa. In Press.
8. Belding, H. S., Darling, R. C., Griffin, D. R., Robinson, S., and Turrell, E. S. 1945. C.A.M. Report No. 390. National Research Council, Feb. 1, 1945.
9. ——, Russell, H. D., and Darling, R. C. 1946. *Federation Proceedings,* Fed. of Amer. Soc. for Exper. Biol., *5,* 7.
10. Benedict, F. G. 1916. *Amer. Jour. Physiol., 41,* 275.
11. ——, and Cathcart, E. P. 1913. *Muscular Work.* Carnegie Institution of Washington, Publication 107.
12. Blum, H. F. 1945. *Physiol. Rev., 25,* 483.
13. Bohnenkamp, H., et al. 1931. *Pflüger's Archiv., 228,* 40, 63, 79, 100, 125.
14. Brunt, D. 1943. *Quarterly Jour. Royal Meteorological Society, 69,* 77.
15. ——. 1945. *Nature, 155,* 559.
16. ——. 1947. *Proc. Physical Society, 59,* 713.
17. Burton, A. C. 1944. Assoc. Committee on Aviation Medicine, Research Report C–2753, Nov. 16, 1944, 159.
18. ——. 1946. *Federation Proceedings,* Fed. of Amer. Soc. for Exper. Biol., *5,* 344.
19. Büttner, K. 1934. *Veröffentlichungen des Preussischen Meteorologischen Instituts,* No. 404, *10,* No. 5.
20. Cole, Rufus, et al. 1931. *Amer. Jour. Hyg., 14,* 49.

21. Collins, S. D. 1934. *Public Health Reports, 49,* 1015.
22. Committee on the Hygiene of Housing (A.P.H.A.). 1938. *Amer. Jour. Pub. Health,* 28, 351.
23. Departmental Committee on Humidity and Ventilation in Cotton Weaving Sheds. 1909 and 1911. HMH Stationery Office, Great Britain.
24. Dill, D. B. 1938. *Life, Heat, and Altitude.* Harvard University Press.
25. Doull, J. A. 1928. *Amer. Jour. Hyg.,* 8, 633.
26. DuBois, E. F. 1936. *Basal Metabolism in Health and Disease.* Lea and Febiger, Philadelphia, Pa.
27. —— 1937. The Mechanism of Heat Loss and Temperature Regulation. Lane Medical Lectures, Stanford University. *Medical Science,* 3, No. 4.
28. Dufton, A. F. 1930. *Physiological Magazine,* 59, 858.
29. Eichna, L. W., Ashe, W. F., Bean, W. B., and Shelly, W. B. 1945. *Jour. Ind. Hyg. and Toxicol.,* 27, 59.
30. ——, Bean, W. B., Ashe, W. F., and Nelson, N. R. 1945. *Bull. Johns Hopkins Hospital,* 76, 25.
31. Eulenberg-Weiner, E. 1938. *Fearfully and Wonderfully Made.* Macmillan Company, New York.
32. Fourt, L., and Harris, M. *Physiology of Human Heat Regulation.* (Edited by L. H. Newburgh.) W. B. Saunders, Philadelphia, Pa. In Press.
33. Gagge, A. P. 1936. *Amer. Jour. Physiol.,* 116, 656.
34. ——. 1937. *Amer. Jour. Physiol.,* 120, 277.
35. ——, Burton, A. C., and Bazett, H. C. 1941. *Science,* 94, 428.
36. ——, and Herrington, L. P. 1947. *Annual Review of Physiology,* 9, 409.
37. ——, ——, and Winslow, C.-E. A. 1937. *Amer. Jour. Hyg.,* 26, 84.
38. ——, Winslow, C.-E. A., and Herrington, L. P. 1938. *Amer. Jour. Physiology,* 124, 30.
39. Goldberger, J., Wheeler, G. A., and Sydenstricker, E. 1920. *Pub. Health Reports,* 35, 648.
40. Goldwasser, R., and Kligler, I. J. 1936. *Jour. Prev. Med.,* 4, 361.
41. Gray, G. 1913. A Study of the Effect of Intra-Seasonal Variations in Weather on Mortality from Various Causes. Doctoral Dissertation, Yale University Library.
42. Greenberg, D. 1919. *Jour. A. M. A.,* 72, 252.
43. Gover, M. 1938. *Pub. Health Reports,* 53, 1122.

44. ——, Reed, L. J., and Collins, S. D. 1934. *Pub. Health Reports, 49,* 811.
45. Hall, J. F. 1946. *Federation Proceedings,* Fed of Amer. Soc. for Exper. Biol., 5, 40.
46. Harding, L. A. and Willard, A. C. 1929. *Mechanical Equipment of Buildings.* John Wiley & Sons, New York.
47. Hardy, J. D. 1934. *Jour. Clin. Investigation, 13,* 593.
48. ——. *Physiology of Human Heat Regulation.* Edited by L. H. Newburgh. W. B. Saunders, Philadelphia. In Press.
49. ——, and DuBois, E. F. 1938. *Jour. Nutrition, 15,* 477.
50. ——, and DuBois, E. F. 1940. *Proc. National Academy of Science, 26,* 389.
51. ——, Milhorat, A. T., and DuBois, E. F. 1938. *Jour. Nutrition, 6,* 583.
52. Heidel, W. A. 1911. *Antecedents of Greek Corpuscular Theories.* Harvard Studies in Classical Philology. Harvard University.
53. Henderson, Y., and Haggard, H. W. 1925. *Amer. Jour. Physiol., 72,* 264.
54. Herrington, L. P. 1947. *Yale Jour. Biol., and Med., 19,* 735.
55. ——, and Moriyama, I. M. 1938. *Amer. Jour. Hyg., 28,* 396.
56. ——, Winslow, C.-E. A., and Gagge, A. P. 1937. *Amer. Jour. Physiol., 120,* 133.
57. Hess, A. F., and Unger, L. J. 1922. *Amer. Jour. Diseases of Children, 24,* 327.
58. Hill, Leonard. 1919. *The Science of Ventilation and Open Air Treatment.* (Great Britain). Medical Research Council Special Report Series, No. 32.
59. ——, and Muecke, L. B. 1913. *Lancet, 1,* 1291.
60. Hippocrates. *The General Works of Hippocrates.* Trans. by Francis Adams. Sydenham Society, London. 1849.
61. Hirsch, A. *Handbook of Geographical and Historical Pathology.* Trans. by Charles Creighton, Sydenham Society, London. 1883–86.
62. Houghten, F. C., Teague, W. W., Miller, W. E., and Yant, W. P. 1929. *Transactions A.S.H.V.E., 35,* 245.
63. ——, ——, ——, and ——. 1931. *Transactions A.S.H.V.E., 37,* 541.
64. Housing Commission of the Health Organization of the League of Nations. 1937. *Quart. Bull. of the Health Organization of the League of Nations, 6,* 505.
65. Huntington, Ellsworth. 1913. *Civilization and Climate.* Yale University Press.

66. —— 1919. *World Power and Evolution.* Yale University Press.
67. Industrial Fatigue Research Board (Great Britain). 1922. Third Annual Report.
68. Justin, M. M. 1923. The Effect of Weather on Health as Shown by a Study of the Mortality Statistics in New York City for the Years 1883–1888. Doctoral Dissertation, Yale University Library.
69. Kraut, H. A., and Muller, E. A. 1946. *Science, 104,* 495.
70. Lavoisier, A. L., and Laplace, P. S. de. 1783. *Memoires de l'Academie Royale des Sciences, 85,* 355.
71. Lefèvre, I. 1911. *Chaleur Animale et Bioénergetique.* Masson et Cie. Paris.
72. Liebig, J. von. 1842. *Die Organische Chemie in ihrer Anwendung auf Physiologie und Pathologie.* Braunschweig.
73. Lorenzi, R. J., Herrington, L. P., and Winslow, C.-E. A. 1946. *Heating, Piping and Air-Conditioning, 18,* 109.
74. Lusk, Graham. 1933. *Nutrition.* Clin. Medica X. Paul B. Hoeber, New York.
75. Markham, F. S. 1947. *Climate and the Energy of Nations.* Second Amer. Ed. Oxford Press.
76. McConnell, W. J., and Houghten, F. C. 1923. *Transactions A.S.H.V.E., 29,* 129.
77. ——, ——, and Yagloglou, C. P. 1924. *Transactions A.S.H.V.E. 30,* 167.
78. ——, and Yagloglou, C. P. 1925. *Transactions A.S.H.V.E., 31,* 101.
79. McLure, J. R. 1924. *Ventilation in School Buildings.* Little and Ives Co., New York.
80. Missenard, A. 1940. *La Chaleur Animale.* Presses Universitaires de France. Paris.
81. Moriyama, I. M., and Herrington, L. P. 1938. *Amer. Jour. Hyg., 28,* 423.
82. Mills, C. A. 1930a. *Arch. Int. Med., 46,* 569.
83. ——. 1930b. *Arch. Int. Med., 46,* 741.
84. ——. 1932a. *Amer. Jour. Hyg., 15,* 573.
85. ——. 1932b. *Endocrinology, 16,* 52.
86. ——. 1934. *Trans Amer. Clin. & Climat. Assoc., 50,* 27.
87. ——. 1936. *International Clinics, 2,* 143.
88. Mudd, S., Goldman, W., and Grant, S. B. 1921. Jour. Exper. Med., 34, 11.
89. ——, Grant, S. B., and Goldman, W. 1921. *Amer. Jour. Otology, Rhinology, and Laryngology, 30,* 1.
90. Murlin, J. R. 1939. *Ergebnisse der Physiologie, 42,* 154.

91. ——, and Burton, A. C. 1935. *Jour. Nutrition, 9,* 356.
92. Nelbach, J. H., and Herrington, L. P. 1942. *Science, 95,* 387.
93. Newburgh, L. H., Johnston, N. W., Lishmet, F. H., and Sheldon, J. M. 1937. *Jour. Nutrition, 13,* 203.
94. ——, ——, Wiley, F. H., Sheldon, J. M., and Murrill, W. A. 1937. *Jour. Nutrition, 13,* 193.
95. New York State Commission on Ventilation. 1923. *Report on Ventilation.* E. P. Dutton and Company, New York.
96. Nichol, E. S. 1936. *Jour. Lab. and Clin. Med., 21,* 588.
97. Nielsen, M. 1938. *Skand. Arch. f. Physiol., 79,* 193.
98. North, C. E. 1913. *Amer. Jour. Pub. Health, 3,* 222.
99. Nungester, W. J., and Klepsen, R. G. 1938. *Jour. Bact., 35,* 32.
100. Oppel, T. W., and Hardy, J. D. 1945. *Jour. Clin. Investigation, 24,* 712.
101. Parr, L. W., Goodale, R. H., and Kirschner, H. 1930. *Jour. Prev. Med., 4,* 39.
102. Péclet, J. C. E. 1904. *Traité de la Chaleur* (1860). Translated into English by Paulding. Van Nostrand, New York.
103. Pettenkofer, M. v. 1877. *Populäre Vorträge.* Vieweg and Sohn, Braunschweig.
104. Plummer, J. H. 1944. *Publ. of the Climatology and Environmental Protection Branch, O.Q.M.G.* August 25, 1944.
105. Pritchard, J. C., Handisyde, C. C., and Rowse, R. H. 1946. *Domestic Heating in America.* Report of the Joint Committee from the Ministry of Fuel and Power and the Department of Scientific Industrial Research, HMH Stationery Office, London.
106. Ranson, S. W., Clark, G., and Magoun, H. W. 1939. *Jour. Lab. and Clin. Med., 25,* 160.
107. Reese, W. H. 1941. *Jour. Text. Inst. Manchester. Trans. 32,* 149.
108. Robertson, H. McG. 1923. *Pub. Health Reports, 58,* 1519.
109. Robinson, S. 1944. *O.S.R.D. Report, CMR m,* No. 12, May 14, 1944.
110. ——, Turrell, E. S., and Gerking, S. D. *Amer. Jour. Physiol., 143,* 21.
111. Rodee, E. J. 1940. *Architectural Forum, 72,* 161.
112. Rowley, F. B., Jordan, R. C., and Snyder, W. E. 1947. *Heating, Piping and Air-Conditioning, 19,* 113.
113. Sedgwick, W. T. and Winslow, C.-E. A. 1902. *Memoirs Amer. Acad. Arts and Sciences, 12,* August, 1902.

114. Seeley, L. E. 1940. *Heating, Piping and Air-Conditioning,* 12, 377.

115. Sherman, H. C. 1946. *Chemistry of Food and Nutrition.* VII. ed. Macmillan, New York.

116. Shulman, L. E. 1945. Biophysical Factors Involved in the Protective Influence of Clothing. Doctoral Dissertation, Yale University Library.

117. Simmons, J. S., et al. 1944. *Global Epidemiology.* Lippincott, Philadelphia.

118. Spealman, J. B., and Chamberlain, N. H. 1930. *Jour. Text. Inst. Trans.,* 21, 29.

119. Stern, F. 1932. *Deut. Med. Woch.,* 58, 1, 298.

120. Strong, R. P. 1935. *Science,* 82, 307.

121. Taylor, C. L. 1945. *Federation Proceedings,* Fed. Amer. Soc. Exper. Biol., 4, 70.

122. ——, and Margarger, J. P. 1946. *Federation Proceedings,* Fed. Amer. Soc. Exper. Biol., 5, 104.

123. Vernon, H. M. 1921. *Industrial Fatigue and Efficiency.* G. Routledge and Sons, London. E. P. Dutton, New York.

124. ——. 1932. *Proc. Inst. Heating and Ventilating* (England), 31, 100.

125. ——. 1934. *The Principles of Heating and Ventilation.* E. Arnold, London.

126. Winslow, C.-E. A. 1902. *Quart. Bull. Amer. Stat. Assoc.* 8, 103.

127. ——. 1926. *Fresh Air and Ventilation.* E. P. Dutton, New York.

128. ——, et al. 1942. Second Report of the A.S.H.V.E. Technical Advisory Committee on Physiological Reactions. *Transactions A.S.H.V.E.* 48, 317.

129. ——, and Bellinger, R. R. 1945. *Bull. of the History of Med.* 17, 127.

130. ——, and Gagge, A. P. 1937. *Amer. Jour. Physiol.,* 129, 1.

131. ——, and Gagge, A. P. 1941. *Amer. Jour. Physiol.,* 134, 664.

132. ——, ——, Greenburg, L., Moriyama, I. M., and Rodee, E. J. 1935. *Amer. Jour. Hyg.,* 22, 137.

133. ——, ——, and Herrington, L. P. 1939. *Amer. Jour. Physiol.,* 127, 505.

134. ——, ——, ——, 1940. *Amer. Jour. Physiol.,* 131, 79.

135. ——, and Greenburg, L. 1918. *Amer. Jour. Pub. Health,* 8, 159.

136. ——, ——. 1932. *Amer. Jour. Hyg.,* 15, 1.

137. ——, Herrington, L. P., and Gagge, A. P. 1936a. *Amer. Jour. Physiol., 116,* 641.

138. ——, ——, ——. 1936b. *Amer. Jour. Physiol., 116,* 669.

139. ——, ——, ——. 1937a. *Amer. Jour. Physiol., 120,* 1.

140. ——, ——, ——. 1937b. *Amer. Jour. Physiol., 120,* 288.

141. ——, ——, ——. 1937c. *Amer. Jour. Hyg., 26,* 103.

142. ——, ——, ——. 1938a. *Amer. Jour Physiol., 124, 51.*

143. ——, ——, ——. 1938b. *Amer. Jour. Physiol., 124,* 692.

144. ——, ——, ——. 1939. *Amer. Jour. Physiol., 127,* 505.

145. ——, ——, and Lorenzi, R. J. 1945. *Transactions A.S.H.V.E., 51,* 197.

146. ——, ——, and Nelbach, J. H. 1942. *Amer. Jour. Hyg., 35,* 27.

147. ——, and Nelbach, P. E. 1946. *Heating and Ventilation Requirements for New York State Schools.* University of the State of New York Press. Albany.

148. ——, and Palmer, G. T. 1915. *Proc. Soc. Exper. Biol., and Med., 12,* 141.

149. Wells, W. W. 1944. *Amer. Jour. Hyg., 40,* 279.

150. Yaglou, C. P., Riley, E. C., and Coggins, D. I. 1936. *Transactions A.S.H.V.E., 42,* 133.

151. Young, M. 1924. *Jour. Hyg., 23,* 151.

INDEX

270